BERTRAND RUSSELL ON THE PHILOSOPHY OF SCIENCE

THE LIBRARY OF LIBERAL ARTS
Oskar Piest, Founder

ON THE PHILOSOPHY
OF SCIENCE

BERTRAND RUSSELL

Edited, with an Introduction, by

CHARLES A. FRITZ, JR.
University of Connecticut

The Library of Liberal Arts

published by

THE BOBBS-MERRILL COMPANY, INC.
A Subsidiary of Howard W. Sams & Co., Inc.
Publishers • Indianapolis • New York • Kansas City

CONTENTS

BERTRAND RUSSELL
ON THE PHILOSOPHY OF SCIENCE

INTRODUCTION

I

The philosophy of science focuses attention on a set of problems some of which made their introduction in Greek philosophy, some of which have emerged only with the advance of science in the twentieth century. For convenience, the problems can be divided into three groups: (1) the relation of science as an activity to other human activities, such as education, religion, social organization; (2) the analysis of crucial notions in science, such as cause, scientific inference, explanation, the nature of scientific laws and theories; (3) the characteristics of the world pictured by science, that is, the structure of the universe and the nature of its ultimate components as shown by the most recent scientific advances. Though Bertrand Russell has written about problems in the first two groups, as a few of the selections below will indicate, his primary concern has been with those problems in group (3). The more extensive treatments have been chosen from this latter group.

The investigation of issues in the philosophy of science usually leads to problems of a general philosophical nature. In many cases the investigator to begin with has a general philosophical background, and works out his analyses of the philosophy of science against it. This is the case in Russell's work. Much of his discussion would be unintelligible without some knowledge of the philosophical beliefs underlying it, and in his books specifically on the philosophy of science, he discusses epistemological and metaphysical questions at considerable length. In the present selections I have tried to include enough of this material to make his point of view clear. Further, since Russell has been writing on philosophy for the past seventy years, it is not at all surprising if within that time his views should have undergone some development. The present writings are from different periods of his thought and reflect what I believe are the important stages.

In the following discussion, I shall briefly outline Russell's general position, and try to indicate some of the significant changes in his views.

II

The three principal aspects of Russell's thought that I shall consider here are (1) his pluralism and metaphysical realism, (2) his epistemology, and (3) the basis and justification of scientific beliefs. These are the three aspects that are most important for his philosophy of science.

1. During the latter part of the nineteenth century, British philosophers were greatly influenced by the Idealist position as found in Hegel and his later British admirers. Russell as a young man turned first to Idealism, but shortly reacted violently against that tradition. To the Idealist, 'mind' is the primary reality in the universe, and mental entities are the most significant. The Idealist emphasizes unity and wholeness in objects and events, and believes that the analysis of a thing into its components or parts involves loss of some of the essential characteristics. When Russell abandoned Idealism, he became with a vengeance a logical realist and a pluralist, emphasizing individuality, diversity, and separateness. The 'real' entities in the world were no longer seen as mental, and analysis became for him the true method for revealing the nature of things.

To determine what the 'real' things in the world are, Russell adopted a procedure that at first seemed relatively simple. It appeared necessary only to find the correct logical form for our statements about the world, and we would then find that the real things of the world would correspond to the constituents of these statements. Thus we must, as Russell said, 'analyze' our beliefs to find their correct form and their constituents. Although when he wrote *Principles of Mathematics* in 1903 this analysis seemed to pose no great difficulty, it shortly turned out to be a more complex procedure than had at first been suspected, and other philosophers quickly became interested. Controversies surrounded the notion of 'analysis,' with Moore, Wittgenstein, Russell, and their critics contributing to the discussion.

When Russell wrote *Principles of Mathematics* he found that there are many 'real' things. "A man, a moment, a number, a class, a relation, a chimera, or anything else that can be mentioned"[1] has Being, and is an individual, an entity. We can think and talk about ordinary material objects, e.g., tables and chairs. They are real. We can think and talk and make statements about numbers and even fictitious objects such as chimeras. They, too, are 'real.' Russell very soon began to doubt that all the things in this list had Being; but even though he found ways to reduce the extent of the list considerably, a belief in the reality and objectivity of the world has never deserted him.

A procedure of analysis that indicated the way in which the number of entities in the world could be drastically reduced was discovered by Russell after the publication of *Principles of Mathematics,* in the course of his logical investigations. His inquiries in this field culminated in *Principia Mathematica* (1910-1913, in collaboration with A. N. Whitehead). The most famous example of this new procedure of 'logical constructions' was his 'theory of descriptions.' This 'theory' was really an analysis and clarification of descriptive phrases of the form "the so-and-so," e.g., "the black cat with yellow eyes," which occur in such statements as "the black cat with yellow eyes was here last night." In *Principles of Mathematics,* subjects of statements were presumed to refer to real entities, and since a descriptive phrase can serve as the subject of a statement, a descriptive phrase was presumed to refer to a real entity. It is rather puzzling to determine precisely what kind of entity this can be. One possibility is that it is the same entity as that referred to by a proper name. If this is the case, then, if the cat in my example is named

[1] Bertrand Russell, *Principles of Mathematics* (Cambridge: University Press, 1903), p. 43.

"Mahal," the phrase "the black cat with yellow eyes" could be replaced by "Mahal," but this involves a loss of meaning. If they had the same meaning, then "the black cat with yellow eyes is Mahal" would mean the same as "Mahal is Mahal," which is a triviality. It would seem that the descriptive phrase, "the black cat with yellow eyes," does not refer to a real cat, as does the proper name "Mahal." If it does not refer to a real cat, then the phrase apparently refers to some odd kind of entity whose existence we accept primarily on the ground that it provides a referent for descriptive phrases.

With Russell's new analysis of descriptive phrases, a 'correct' form for statements employing descriptive phrases can be found. Using my previous example, the phrase, "the black cat with yellow eyes," no longer occurs as a constituent of the statement, "the black cat with yellow eyes was here last night," but instead the statement becomes (roughly), "there is one and only one thing which is a cat and has yellow eyes and is black and was here last night." It is now unnecessary to assume the existence of a unique entity corresponding to the descriptive phrase. Upon analysis the statement is found to refer only to conventionally real entities. Reference is made only to concepts, whose existence to Russell is not at all puzzling.

The theory of descriptions offers a definite semantic advantage by clarifying the meaning of descriptive phrases. To Russell it had the further metaphysical advantage of reducing the number of real entities which are assumed to exist. Entities which are referents of definite descriptions are now to be excused from the roster of the real. Russell found that the method of constructions could be applied to other terms besides descriptions, e.g., numbers and classes, with the result that these terms, although capable of being the grammatical subjects of statements, are no longer seen as denoting real entities. The 'correct' logical form of a statement came to be removed further and further from its superficial form, and a simple inspection of statements in their ordinary or common-sense form no longer sufficed to reveal the ultimate entities of the world.

Suppose now that this method is applied to statements referring to scientific entities, such as 'points,' 'instants,' and 'electrons.' An analysis of such statements no longer requires that such terms refer to existent entities, if some construction by means of a different kind of entity can be found to replace them. One task of the philosophy of science, in Russell's view, is to provide such an analysis wherever possible, to determine which are the irreducible, or ultimate, real entities.

2. In addition to a theory concerning the reality of various kinds of entities in the world, one requires an account of how knowledge of them is arrived at. Russell's theory of knowledge is basically in the tradition of British empiricism. Within this tradition, the individual's knowledge of the world is obtained by means of his senses, and is based upon what are often called his 'sense data' or 'percepts.' In Russell's view the individual has in addition some a priori knowledge of general concepts and principles of logic. However, for Russell knowledge of things and events in the world, 'empirical' knowledge, is based on the individual's sense experience, which is constituted by his sense data.

Sense data are a stumbling block to the naïve realism of un-critical common sense. The naïve realist assumes that what one meets through his sense experience are things, trees, houses, people; but considerable attention in philosophy since the seventeenth century has been devoted to arguing that this cannot be the case. Instead it is argued that what one encounters directly in experience are not permanent, publicly observable objects, but his own *experience* of them, his view of a house, his hearing of other people, his own feelings. Even these experiences can be further broken down. Our visual experience of a house is actually composed of our momentary experiences of patches of various shapes and colors; our tactual experiences of the house would be the feelings of wood and of glass and of masonry. At different times, under different conditions of observation, the sensations we receive might very well differ. These momentary experiences have been called 'sense data' or 'percepts' by recent philosophers. Sense data include patches of color, snatches of sound, and are what comprise the individual's sensible experience. They vary with the individual's physiological and psychological constitution, and with the conditions of observation.

The principal reasons that led to the adoption of this analysis of experience can, I believe, be summed up by two arguments. (a) The scientific account of the process of perception, involving an intervening medium, and various complex physiological processes in the observer, make it difficult to understand how the observer could simply or directly observe external objects as they really are, as if his senses were merely open windows. (b) The relativity and subjectivity of perception, to however slight an extent, still makes perception an individual matter. Thus different individuals frequently experience the 'same' objects slightly differently, and on occasion, for example, in dreams and hallucinations, one observer will 'see' something that no one else does. It is difficult to understand how a naïve realist could claim to observe the object as it really is in itself and apart from being perceived, and yet explain subjective variations in perception.

Granting the helpful sophistication of the sense-data analysis of experience, can we on this hypothesis be said to 'know,' in any sense, permanent, external, physical objects? To most philosophers who hold this view it was reasonable to infer that external objects exist which 'cause' our sense data, and that changes in the objects would cause different sense data in us. Descartes believed that we could have confidence in the existence of external objects causing sense data because God would not deceive us in so fundamental a respect. Hume, on the other hand, maintained that, although we might believe in the existence of external objects, we could have no conclusive rational reason for doing so. Recent philosophers have examined the details of this 'causal' theory of perception in considerable detail.

Russell's conclusions relative to this matter have undergone some change during the course of his writing. When he wrote *The Problems of Philosophy* (1912), the belief that there were external objects corresponding to our sense data was an "instinctive belief," and "since this belief . . . tends to simplify and systematize our account of our experiences, there seems no good reason for rejecting it,"[1] a view close in spirit to that of Descartes. A short time later, in *Our Knowledge of the External World* (1914), he decided that a belief in an external cause of our perceptions, "instinctive" or not, was unnecessary. As I shall discuss more fully below, he maintained that the assumption of the existence of external objects served no useful purpose. However, by the time he wrote *The Analysis of Matter* (1927), he had returned to his earlier acceptance of a causal theory, now giving it a reasoned defense rather than accepting it merely as an "instinctive" belief. To the best of my knowledge he has continued to accept such a theory.

3. I have briefly reviewed reasons directing Russell to the conclusion that empirical knowledge is based upon the individual's sense experience, or sense data. Sense data at best, however, only give us knowledge of individual occurrences; Russell saw that we need in addition some account of the manner in which knowledge of individual events can be used as a basis for formulating and confirming general laws and theories in the sciences. It is maintained by many writers that in addition to knowledge derived from sense data, some general principle, the usual candidate being the "principle of induction," is required to allow us to infer from various individual instances of phenomena to general laws. Thus, for example, if we observe some actual cats, and find that all that we observe have claws, the "principle of induction" validates the inference to "all cats (without exception) have claws." The justification for our acceptance of the principle itself is a further, and highly controversial, question.

This matter is discussed in many of the following selections. In his earlier writings Russell accepted the principle of induction as an assumption, justifiable in terms of its utility; in his later writings he came to believe that the one principle should be discarded in favor of a more complex analysis, and argued for the acceptance of several "postulates" which would validate inferences from various types of individual occurrences to scien-

1 Bertrand Russell, *The Problems of Philosophy* (New York: H. Holt, 1912), p. 38.

tific laws. Russell's most recent view is in "Non-Demonstrative Inference," in Part Five below.

Once the general principle or principles necessary to scientific inference are found, one can proceed to a detailed examination of scientific knowledge, showing what sense data (observations) underlie it, and precisely what further principles have been employed in arriving at the conclusions. But not only did Russell wish to make clear the principles used in justifying scientific knowledge; at an early period in his writings he also sought 'certainty,' or sought to avoid wherever possible those beliefs and principles which are not 'certain.' Russell admires Descartes for the latter's attempt to provide a reconstruction of knowledge which will base it as far as possible on 'certainties.' Descartes 'doubted' many obvious common-sense beliefs, but his 'doubt,' rather than being a rejection of these beliefs, was a demand to find a sound reason for believing them. Descartes provided what he thought was an adequate criterion of a 'sound' or 'certain' belief, and attempted to show how all knowledge could be grounded on sound beliefs. Russell at this early period attempted to do the same thing, using different criteria of 'certainty.'

It is difficult to explain what philosophers who talk about 'certain' beliefs have in mind. It is not certainty in the ordinary sense of having complete confidence in a belief, but 'certain' in the sense that a 'certain' belief cannot conceivably be false. It must be true either because its denial would be logically self-contradictory, or, as is the case with beliefs based on sense data, because the evidence for the belief is complete and there is no further evidence that would conceivably be relevant. Russell maintained that beliefs concerning our sense data are certain, and since these are the basis of scientific knowledge, that scientific knowledge at least rests on a 'certain' base. His goal at this time was to provide a rigorous reconstruction of scientific knowledge. Where it might not be possible to eliminate questionably grounded arguments and inferences, at least he felt they could be revealed to public inspection and stigmatized by being labeled as 'risky' inferences.

Whether or not this drive to find 'certain' knowledge, a desire for knowledge that *cannot* be doubted, is a legitimate quest is a point which has often been seriously questioned. Most people are content with knowledge which is judged reliable by criteria employed by reasonable people in everyday affairs; but for some, such vague standards are insufficient; their temperament directs them to settle only for the ideal—knowledge which *cannot* be false. Russell himself in his later writings does not stress this ideal of 'certainty' to the extent that he did at an earlier time; he is still interested in examining the structure of scientific knowledge, but is not as concerned to reduce it to 'certain' elements.

III

Russell's philosophy of science was developed against the philosophical background outlined above. It, too, underwent some modification. I shall discuss first his earlier view, found principally in *Our Knowledge of the External World* (1914), and in several essays written about the same time and since reprinted in *Mysticism and Logic*.

Physics is generally accepted as being an empirical science, and as such must be based upon experience. For Russell, the basic elements of knowledge are beliefs based on the sense data comprising an individual's sense experience. These elements are 'certain,' are the indubitable foundation upon which his remaining beliefs are based, other beliefs being inferred by the help of various assumed principles. One aim of Russell's philosophy of science is to show how scientific laws and theories are confirmed by sense data, and what further principles are required to justify our acceptance of them. When this is accomplished, not only, Russell hopes, will it be made clear how science is based upon experience, but also how far science can be based upon 'certain' beliefs. Further, Russell's philosophy of science specifies what Russell finds to be the ultimate, real entities of the universe and determines how sense data and scientific objects are related to them.

In the earlier period, Russell found that with the help of his recently discovered method of 'logical constructions,' a neat, simple view of science and the real world could be formulated. In brief, the ultimate entities of the world *are* our sense data; common-sense material objects and scientific objects are both constructions from sense data—no further 'real' entities need be assumed.

To clarify, suppose we consider how one can move from a common-sense view of an object to an interpretation of it as a construction from sense data. We can see an object, hear it, touch it, taste it; all of these experiences of the object are sense data. As an example, assume that I have a coffee cup in front of me. Confining the discussion to sight, I have visual sense data constituting the way the cup looks at any given moment. There will be sense data of its color, its shape, its pattern, its luster. At other moments I will have different, but similar visual sense data occasioned by the cup being in a different position, by my changing position, by changes in the illumination, or some other change. A slight change in position will result in sense data very similar to the original; a greater change will probably result in less similar sense data. I could, in principle at least, make these changes of sense data into a continuous series, either by slowly moving the cup (or myself) through intermediate positions and attending to the sense data received during these changes, or by imagining and projecting what sense data at intermediate positions would be like.

The theory of knowledge that Russell adopts maintains that our knowledge of material objects is based on sense data obtained in the manner illustrated in the preceding example, and that any further knowledge of those objects is an inference from sense data. We do not experience the apparent substantiality, permanence, and objectivity of ordinary things; we can experience nothing besides momentary and subjective sense data. It might be objected that other people can see my coffee cup, and that this proves its objectivity. But what these observers experience of the coffee cup are sense data very similar to my own, if they are observing it under similar conditions. Their sense data can be correlated with mine; if I have a cup-like sense datum in my right visual field another observer to my right would have a similar sense datum in his left visual field. If both of us move toward the cup, our sense data of the cup would occupy a relatively larger part of our visual fields. We can talk about the 'same' cup because we are both having similar sense data. It might further be objected that we can talk and think about the cup when it is not present and we are having no sense data of it, or speak of what it would be like if—if it were broken, for example. This situation, too, can be explained in terms of sense data, not actually experienced sense data, but imaginary, or 'hypothetical' sense data. We can visualize what the cup would look like if it were here, when in fact no cuplike sense data are present; put it in front of me and in fact I have sense data very similar to those I anticipated. These 'hypothetical' sense data can also be correlated with the ones actually received by different observers.

We do, however, speak of the cup as being *one* thing, not as many individual sense data. Russell's success with logical constructions had shown, he believed, that the fact that we can speak of something as being *one* thing does not at all imply that there must be some actual unity. Sentences referring to objects by means of descriptive phrases, sentences referring to numbers or classes, can be analyzed to show that they refer not to these presumed simple entities but instead to other, different, entities. Let us apply this analysis to the coffee cup. On the basis of their similarity, collect my visual sense data of the cup into a group, add to that group my sense data of the cup from other senses, add the sense data of other observers of the cup, which is possible because of their correlation with my sense data, and add finally the hypothetical sense data that could be obtained under conditions where in fact no sense data are obtained: the whole group of sense data, Russell maintains, we can take to be the cup. Anything that could be said by means of the presumed thing 'cup' can now be said by means of this group of sense data. There is no useful purpose served in affirming the existence of a unique entity 'cup' distinct from the sense data that we experience. (The account here given of the construction of common-sense objects is only an outline; Russell's detailed exposition is reprinted in Part Two below.)

Scientific entities for Russell can be constructed in an analogous manner. Form the group of sense data which constitute what observers know of the entity by sense experience, however indirect that experience may be, add to it whatever hypothetical sense data are relevant, and the result is a group, or set, of sense data which satisfies all the purposes that were served by assuming the existence of a scientific entity.

Russell had now arrived at a view of the world which resolves the basic problem of the philosophy of science by showing that the world is composed of sense data, which are individual, discrete entities; we speak of some groups of sense data as material objects, of other groups as scientific objects. There is no question as to how we obtain knowledge of these objects: they are groups of sense data, and it is sense data that we know with certainty. For this reason we can confirm statements about common-sense things, and likewise scientific laws. Russell saw the reconstruction of our knowledge as now resting upon a secure base, namely, sense data, and although various principles of reasoning had to be employed which are not certain, at least they had been made explicit.

In spite of the measure of success which this view enjoyed in meeting technical philosophical difficulties, it results in what may seem to many people a curious view of the world. Permanent objects have vanished, leaving us with a world composed of sense data which are subjective, fragmentary entities. Russell meets this objection not by arguing that his view must be true, but that it *could* be true; why insist on the existence of permanent substances if sense data will do just as well? If one wishes to believe in permanent substances, Russell will not take issue with him, beyond pointing out that he thinks they serve no useful purpose.

IV

Accepting Russell's analysis of material objects outlined above, we find we can talk about the coffee cup in terms of sense data, without supposing the existence of a single entity, 'cup.' Everything we can say about the cup—that it is in front of me, that it is empty, that it is round—can be said by employing only sense data. Thus, "the cup is yellow" becomes (very roughly) "yellow sense-datum is member of group of sense data called 'cup.'" However, there is one type of statement about the cup which is much more difficult to translate into sense-data language than examples I have used so far. We can speak of my perceptual experience as being *caused* by the cup, e.g., I see a cup because one has been placed in front of me, or, several observers all have similar cup data because a cup has been placed in front of them. But, further, the cup can have effects on other objects: I place the cup upon a piece of paper, and it leaves a mark upon the paper when it is removed. These examples can be analyzed in terms of sense data, e.g., I have data of cup resting on piece of paper, my sense data of its removal are followed by sense data of ring on paper. We do, however, normally think of the cup as in some sense causing our sense data, or that the ring appeared on the paper *because* of the weight of the cup. It is a highly controversial matter whether the 'because' can be adequately translated by means of sense data.

The common-sense view of the world considers the world as a place of various physical causal processes which produce certain effects. No matter how skillful a philosophical view may be technically, if it dispenses with physical objects leaving sense data to act for them, it is disturbing. Russell came to the conclusion that this was a legitimate criticism of his early view, as well as of other examples of phenomenalist theories, including the model of them all, Bishop Berkeley's. Within a few years Russell had abandoned his early view in favor of one that did less violence to common sense.

By the time Russell wrote *The Analysis of Matter* (1927), he had modified his original view to find a place for a material world external to and different from sense data. He maintained the same general philosophical framework I have described in section II above, with the important modification that he allows greater flexibility in his standards of what is to constitute the starting point of acceptable knowledge. Earlier, it had been his aim to base science on 'certain' knowledge, that obtained immediately from sense data, with the help of as few non-certain beliefs as possible. Now, although sense data still provide the certain base, we must also work on the assumption that scientific laws and theories are for the most part true. There are controversial parts of science; but, on the other hand, many scientific results are rarely questioned. For example, science informs us that the earth revolves around the sun, and it certainly seems to be the case that there is in fact an earth and a sun and that they revolve in the manner and in approximately the times calculated by astronomers.

Russell's problem is modified correspondingly. He must now reconcile in detail scientific truths both with our apparent everyday world of material objects and with our percepts. What kind of universe do we have in which scientific theories can be true, and can be shown to be true by our sense data?

Empirical knowledge begins with sense data, which Russell now calls 'percepts.' From these, Russell maintains, we are justified in drawing various conclusions, which earlier he would have maintained were dubious and unacceptable. In my example of the coffee cup being placed before several observers, the fact that they all at approximately the same time begin to receive coffee-cup percepts is now for Russell adequate grounds for believing that there is some real physical object, or series of events, affecting all the percipients. If the cup is left on the desk, and an observer returns later and finds that the coffee in it has become cold, we could say simply that he now has percepts of cold coffee whereas somewhat earlier he had percepts of hot coffee; but Russell feels he is justified in saying more. He would now add that there is a physical coffee, which has changed, producing a change in our percepts. A physical origin of percepts provides an explanation of the fact that mechanical recording devices can 'perceive' in very much the same fashion as human observers do. Russell believes that we are amply justified, even though no strict formal proof can be supplied, in accepting the causal theory of perception, holding that our percepts are caused by an external physical thing or process of some type.

Since it is percepts and not external events that we experience, and know with certainty, Russell sees clearly that the causal theory of perception cannot itself be confirmed by experience. He accepts it because it provides a useful explanation of the order and continuity of percepts. There is, of course, little that we can know about the nature of the external causes. One might suggest that when we have a 'red' percept there is an outside, independent object that is 'red' in precisely the same sense; but most philosophers would not accept this argument, for the reason that originally led them, and Russell, to advocate sense-data theories of knowledge in the first place. And though there may be external differences which are not reflected in corresponding distinguishable percepts (for example, Russell points out that two glasses of water may look alike and yet one will cause typhoid and the other will not), Russell believes that it is at least safe to assume a correlation between changes in our percepts and changing external events. Thus, as my percepts of the coffee cup move relative to my percepts of the desk upon which the cup is placed, I assume that there is a correlated series of events that constitute the cup being moved from one place to another. It is safe, Russell believes, to infer that there is a similarity of structure between our percepts and the events constituting the external world. What we can infer from our percepts about the nature of the events causing them is based on an assumed similarity of structure.

The world, Russell believes, is constituted by a multitude of events, many of them grouped around 'centers.' These we can call 'objects.' They will have 'lines' or 'chains' of events radiating outwards from them which can intersect, or react, with lines from other events, or with observers. When they encounter an observer with appropriate sensory apparatus the last event in the chain will be a percept. Changes in the intervening medium, or in the physiological state of the observer, will constitute modifications in the later events of a chain; the group of events composed of the percept, the preceding events in the chain including those near the 'center,' will be the 'object.' The causal laws of science are based on the interrelations between various chains of events; the mind is a still different chain of events, connected by 'mental' relations, especially memory.

V

The following selections from Russell's writings present his development of the two views of the relation between science and experience that I have just discussed. In addition, several related topics have been included: the nature of logic and mathematics, causation, inference, and the relation of science to education and society. Russell's views on these topics are clear enough to need no further comment.

In conclusion, I shall comment briefly on Russell's contribution to the philosophy of science, singling out two directions from which he might be criticized, and estimating the seriousness of such criticism.

1. The sense-data theory of perception which provides the background and general context for Russell's philosophy of science has been under attack for some time, and many philosophers at present reject it. The sense-data view suffers from the basic implausibility of maintaining that our knowledge of external physical objects is in no way direct, but an inference from sense data; for common sense inclines to the belief of the naïve realist, that one experiences objects in the external world. It would be preferable to have an analysis of perception which holds to the view that one does indeed perceive objects that are external, and yet meet the objections to that view presented in section II above. Various philosophers have recently advanced proposals in this direction.

An extended discussion of theories of perception would lead me far beyond the scope of this Introduction.[1] I am here concerned only with the effect of the controversy on the validity of Russell's philosophy of science. If this theory of knowledge is unsound, then to the extent that his philosophy of science is based upon it, that too will be unsound. Hence any serious objection to his theory of knowledge is also a serious, though not necessarily fatal, objection to his philosophy of science.

His philosophy of science might be rescued in some such manner as follows. Russell's earlier view constructed the world out of sense data, and he attributed a metaphysical significance to this construction. He thought sense data were real existents, the only real entities that need be assumed. If his sense data analysis is not accepted, then the metaphysical consequences of his theory are without support. It is possible, however, to give his early theory a different interpretation than that which Russell himself gives it. We can look at it as without metaphysical import, as merely an attempt to reconcile experience with science. His constructions then become a method of showing the manner in which scientific terms can be expressed in terms of experience, not for the purpose of determining what they 'really' denote or are, but solely to indicate how the terms apply to experience, and can be verified by it. If Russell's theory is given this interpretation, the epistemological objection loses much of its force.

I am not maintaining that Russell would accept such an interpretation of his work. It does, however, illustrate how it might be possible to modify, or limit Russell's philosophy in such a way that much of significance still remains, in spite of the sound criticisms of the philosophy in its original form.

When we consider Russell's later view, criticisms of his epistemological views are not nearly as damaging. Though we may criticize Russell's theory that immediate knowledge is confined to percepts, all other events being known only by infer-

[1] A good discussion of the different issues involved in perception and the various theories proposed to meet them can be found in R. J. Hirst, *The Problems of Perception* (New York: Humanities Press, 1959).

ence, this need not undermine his view that the world is composed of groups and chains of events. We might modify Russell's epistemology in a way which would require little alteration in the further details of his theory. Russell argues that there is a causal chain from the object to the observer, that the percept is the last event in this causal chain, and that this *last* event is what the observer sees. Then by inference from this last event, the percept, the observer must, according to Russell, determine the preceding events in the chain. If in fact such a causal chain exists, and if in fact the percept is the last event in the chain, it does not follow that this last event is what is seen by the observer. 'Experience' and 'see' are vague and difficult words. The last event in the chain may constitute the observer's 'experience' or 'seeing,' but that might be of such a nature that *what* we 'see,' as distinct from the act or process of seeing, would be the first event in the chain. One might now argue that *what* we 'see' is the first event, and use our apprehension or awareness of this event to infer the existence of the last event, the percept, the means by which we see. It is not my purpose to advocate this theory as a definitive theory of perception, but rather to show that a radical alteration in Russell's theory of knowledge may have little effect upon his final philosophy of science.

2. Russell's philosophy of science comes under attack from a quite different quarter when it is suggested that he misunderstands the nature of scientific theories. Russell assumes that scientific theories are true of the world in a fairly obvious sense of 'true.' The contention of those who hold what is sometimes called an "instrumentalist" view of scientific theories is that theories are not the kind of statements which can be characterized as either 'true' or 'false,' but rather as 'useful.' If science were confined to simple statements such as "all crows eat corn," or "all iron rusts when exposed to moisture," it would not be difficult to maintain that scientific statements are true in the usual sense of the term. We can observe crows and iron and corn and moisture; but the situation is more obscure when we come to scientific statements involving abstract terms. Russell

has tried to interpret abstract terms by means of real entities. The instrumentalist argues that he is missing the point. The instrumentalist would interpret laws and theories not as statements true about the world, but as symbolic devices, 'fictions,' rules or principles of inference. The power of science is that it is a kind of conceptual shorthand that sums up our experience and provides a tool for predicting future experience. Thus for the instrumentalist the molecular account of matter enables us to calculate what amounts of different substances must be used to form some given compound. Whether or not the substances concerned are 'really' composed in the manner suggested is not, for the instrumentalist, important. Scientific theories are seen to be devices that enable man to comprehend and predict the events of the world; in what sense they picture the world or are 'really' like it is irrelevant.[1]

This is not Russell's view of theories. It is clearly the case that scientific theories are useful as aids in comprehending the world and predicting its occurrences, but their usefulness, according to Russell, is grounded on their truth, on their correspondence, in some way or other, to the real world. Russell has attempted to show in what this correspondence consists. He believes that it is too simple to assume that there are real entities, 'molecule,' 'point,' 'meson' and the like. For him, these, like ordinary common-sense objects, are elaborate constructions out of events. Scientific laws and theories are 'true' because they reflect actual patterns of events in the world. We can restate Russell's original problem: assuming that scientific theories are true, not merely useful, but *true*, what must the world be like to make their truth intelligible? It is this question that he has tried to answer by his construction of the world first from sense data, and later from events. The ingenuity and sophistication of Russell's theory have made it a landmark in the philosophy of science.

1 An excellent discussion of the different conceptions of the nature of a scientific theory can be found in Ernest Nagel, *The Structure of Science* (New York: Harcourt, Brace and World, 1961), Chapter VI.

SELECTED READINGS

Principal Works by Bertrand Russell

My Philosophical Development. London: George Allen &
Unwin, and New York: Simon and Schuster, 1959. Contains
an interesting account by Russell of his philosophical development, and also his replies to some recent criticisms of
his philosophy.

ON LOGIC AND THE FOUNDATIONS OF MATHEMATICS:

Principles of Mathematics. Cambridge: University Press, 1903.
2nd edn., with new Introduction, London: George Allen
& Unwin, and New York: W. W. Norton & Co., 1938.

Principia Mathematica, with ALFRED NORTH WHITEHEAD. Cambridge: University Press, 1910-1913. 2nd edn., with new
Introduction, Cambridge: University Press, 1925.

Introduction to Mathematical Philosophy. London: George
Allen & Unwin, and New York: Macmillan Co., 1919.

Logic and Knowledge, ed. R. C. MARSH. London: George Allen
& Unwin, 1956. A collection of Russell's essays most of
which are otherwise obtainable only in periodicals.

ON THE PHILOSOPHY OF SCIENCE:

Our Knowledge of the External World. London: George Allen
& Unwin, and Chicago: Open Court, 1914. 2nd edn., New
York: W. W. Norton, 1929.

Mysticism and Logic. New York: Longman, 1918. London:
George Allen & Unwin, 1929. See especially chapters 6,
7, and 8.

The Analysis of Mind. London: George Allen & Unwin, and
New York: The Macmillan Co., 1921.

The Analysis of Matter. London: George Allen & Unwin, 1927.
New York: Dover Publications, 1954.

Human Knowledge. London: George Allen & Unwin, and New
York: Simon and Schuster, 1948.

GENERAL PHILOSOPHICAL WORKS:

The Problems of Philosophy. New York: H. Holt, 1912.

Our Knowledge of the External World. (See above.)

Mysticism and Logic. (See above.)

"Philosophy of Logical Atomism," *Monist,* 1918-1919. Reprinted in *Logic and Knowledge* (see above.)

Philosophy. New York: W. W. Norton, 1927. Published as *An Outline of Philosophy,* London: George Allen & Unwin, 1927.

An Inquiry into Meaning and Truth. London: George Allen & Unwin, and New York: W. W. Norton, 1940.

Human Knowledge. (See above.)

Secondary Works on Russell's Philosophy

FRITZ, CHARLES A., JR. *Bertrand Russell's Construction of the External World.* London: Routledge and Kegan Paul, and New York: Humanities Press, 1952.

GÖTLIND, ERIK. *Bertrand Russell's Theories of Causation.* Uppsala, 1952.

BRIEFER DISCUSSIONS:

PASSMORE, JOHN. *A Hundred Years of Philosophy.* London: Gerald Duckworth, and New York: Macmillan Co., 1957. Especially recommended.

SCHILPP, PAUL A. (ed.). *The Philosophy of Bertrand Russell.* Evanston and Chicago: Open Court, 1944. Papers by different philosophers on aspects of Russell's philosophy, together with Russell's comments on the papers. Also contains a brief account by Russell of his philosophical development, and a complete bibliography of Russell's writings up to 1944, compiled by LESTER E. DENONN.

URMSON, J. O. *Philosophical Analysis.* London: Oxford University Press, 1956.

WARNOCK, G. J. *English Philosophy Since 1900.* London: Oxford University Press, 1958.

BERTRAND RUSSELL
ON THE PHILOSOPHY OF SCIENCE

PART ONE

Formal and Empirical Science

It is generally acknowledged that the natural sciences are
empirical, that is, that they are based upon observation
and experiment. Whether mathematics should be included
among the empirical sciences has, however, been a dis-
puted question. If mathematics is to be included in the
natural sciences, it must be because the truth of its axioms
and theorems is determined by recourse to experience.
Some writers, e.g., John Stuart Mill, adopt an extreme
empirical approach and argue that mathematics is indeed
true solely on experiential grounds. The preponderance
of opinion, including that of Russell, disagrees, and places
mathematics in a special category, apart from the natural
sciences. For the sake of convenience, mathematics is by
most theorists called a 'formal' science, whose further
characterization remains controversial. Russell maintains
that any science is empirical if its truth depends to any
extent upon perception. In contrast, he believes that the
truth of mathematics and logic is analytic, in no way dependent upon observation or experiment.

The nature of mathematics was one of Russell's early
concerns. In his logical writings, culminating in *Principia
Mathematica* (1910-1913), Russell constructed a logical

3

system within which he derived the basic principles of mathematics. Thus mathematics was 'reduced' to logic and became a part of logic in the sense that it was part of an all-inclusive system whose initial postulates were propositions of logic. Since these logical propositions are tautologies, 'analytically' true, the mathematical propositions which are derived from them are also tautologies, and hence also analytically true.

In the following Chapter One, Russell discusses the nature of empirical science in general and distinguishes it from mathematics. Chapter Two is an account of the nature of mathematics and logic. Chapter Three considers the relation between the abstract concepts that occur in empirical science, and the natural world to which such science applies. Since these sciences are based upon experience, an 'interpretation' of their terms must be given that makes clear their relation to the natural world. Finally, Chapter Four is a detailed investigation of the number of the abstract terms of a science that must be interpreted, whether there is not some 'minimum' number that can be given an interpretation and the remainder defined by their means.

CHAPTER ONE

What Is an Empirical Science?

It would be generally agreed that physics is an empirical science, as contrasted with logic and pure mathematics. I want, in this chapter, to define in what this difference consists.

We may observe, in the first place, that many philosophers in the past have denied the distinction. Thorough-going rationalists have believed that the facts which we regard as only discoverable by observation could really be deduced from logical and metaphysical principles; thorough-going empiricists have believed that the premisses of pure mathematics are obtained by induction from experience. Both views seem to me false, and are, I think, rarely held in the present day; nevertheless, it will be as well to examine the reasons for thinking that there is an epistemological distinction between pure mathematics and physics, before trying to discover its exact nature.

There is a traditional distinction between necessary and contingent propositions, and another between analytic and synthetic propositions. It was generally held before Kant that necessary propositions were the same as analytic propositions, and contingent propositions were the same as synthetic propositions. But even before Kant the two distinctions were different, even if they effected the same division of propositions. It was held that every proposition is necessary, assertoric, or

From *The Analysis of Matter* by Bertrand Russell (1927), Chapter XVII, pp. 169-177. Reprinted through permission of the publishers, George Allen & Unwin Ltd., London; and Dover Publications, Inc., New York 14, N.Y., copyright 1954 by Dover Publications, Inc.

possible, and that these are ultimate notions, comprised under the head of "modality." I do not think much can be made of modality, the plausibility of which seems to have come from confusing propositions with propositional functions. Propositions may, it is true, be divided in a way corresponding to what was meant by analytic and synthetic; this will be explained in a moment. But propositions which are not analytic can only be true or false; a true synthetic proposition cannot have a further property of being necessary, and a false synthetic proposition cannot have the property of being possible. Propositional functions, on the contrary, are of three kinds: those which are true for all values of the argument or arguments, those which are false for all values, and those which are true for some arguments and false for others. The first may be called necessary, the second impossible, the third possible. And these terms may be transferred to propositions when they are not known to be true on their own account, but what is known as to their truth or falsehood is deduced from knowledge of propositional functions. E.g. "it is possible that the next man I meet will be called John Smith" is a deduction from the fact that the propositional function "x is a man and is called John Smith" is possible—i.e. true for some values of x and false for others. Where, as in this instance, it is worth while to say that a *proposition* is possible, the fact rests upon our ignorance. With more knowledge, we should know who is the next man I shall meet, and then it would be certain that he is John Smith or certain that he is not John Smith. Possibility in this sense thus becomes assimilated to probability, and may count as any degree of probability other than 0 and 1. An "assertoric" proposition, similarly, was, I think, a confused notion applicable to a proposition known to be true but also known to be a value of a propositional function which is sometimes false—e.g. "John Smith is bald."

The distinction of analytic and synthetic is much more relevant to the difference between pure mathematics and physics. Traditionally, an "analytic" proposition was one whose contradictory was self-contradictory, or, what came to the same thing in Aristotelian logic, one which ascribed to a subject a predicate which was part of it—e.g. "white horses are horses." In practice, however, an analytic proposition was one whose truth could be known by means of logic alone. This meaning survives, and is still important, although we can no longer use the definition in terms of subject and predicate or that in terms of the law of contradiction. When Kant argued that "$7 + 5 = 12$" is synthetic, he was using the subject-predicate definition, as his argument shows. But when we define an analytic proposition as one which can be deduced from logic alone, then "$7 + 5 = 12$" is analytic. On the other hand, the proposition that the sum of the angles of a triangle is two right angles is synthetic. We must ask ourselves, therefore: What is the common quality of the propositions which can be deduced from the premisses of logic?

The answer to this question given by Wittgenstein in his *Tractatus Logico-Philosophicus* seems to me the right one. Propositions which form part of logic, or can be proved by logic, are all *tautologies*—i.e. they show that certain different sets of symbols are different ways of saying the same thing, or that one set says part of what the other says. Suppose I say: "If p implies q, then not-q implies not-p." Wittgenstein asserts that "p implies q" and "not-q implies not-p" are merely different symbols for one proposition: the fact which makes one true (or false) is the same as the fact which makes the other true (or false). Such propositions, therefore, are really concerned with symbols. We can know their truth or falsehood without studying the outside world, because they are only concerned with symbolic manipulations. I should add—though here Wittgenstein might dissent—that all pure mathematics consists of tautologies in the above sense. If this is true, then obviously empiricists such as J. S. Mill are wrong when they say that we believe $2 + 2 = 4$ because we have found so many instances of its truth that we can make an induction by simple enumeration which has little chance of being wrong. Every unprejudiced person must agree that such a view *feels* wrong: our certainty concerning simple mathematical propositions does not seem analogous to our certainty that the sun will rise tomorrow. I do not mean that we feel more sure of the one than of the other, though perhaps we ought to do so; I mean that our assurance seems to have a different source.

I accept the view, therefore, that some propositions are tautologies and some are not, and I regard this as the distinction underlying the old distinction of analytic and synthetic propositions. It is obvious that a proposition which is a tautology is so in virtue of its form, and that any constants which it may contain can be turned into variables without impairing its tautological quality. We may take as a stock example: "If Socrates is a man and all men are mortal, then Socrates is mortal." This is a value of the general logical tautology:

"For all values of x, a, and β, if x is an a, and all a's are β's, then x is a β."

In logic, it is a waste of time to deal with particular examples of general tautologies; therefore constants ought never to occur, except such as are purely formal. The cardinal numbers turn out to be purely formal in this sense; therefore all the constants of pure mathematics are purely formal.

A proposition cannot be a tautology unless it is of a certain complexity, exceeding that of the simplest propositions. It is obvious that there is more complexity in equating two ways of saying the same thing than there is in either way separately. It is obvious also that, whenever it is actually useful to know that two sets of symbols say the same thing, or that one says part of what the other says, that must be because we have some knowledge as to the truth or falsehood of what is expressed by one of the sets. Consequently logical knowledge would be very unimportant if it stood alone; its importance arises through its combination with knowledge of propositions which are not purely logical.

All the propositions which are not tautologies we shall call "synthetic." The simplest kinds of propositions must be synthetic, in virtue of the above argument. And if logic or pure mathematics can ever be employed in a process leading to knowledge that is not tautological, there must be sources of knowledge other than logic and pure mathematics.

The distinctions hitherto considered in this chapter have been logical. In the case of modality, it is true, we found a certain confusion from an admixture of epistemological notions; but modality was intended to be logical, and in one form it was found to be so. We come now to a distinction which is essentially epistemological, that, namely, between *a priori* and empirical knowledge.

Knowledge is said to be *a priori* when it can be acquired without requiring any fact of experience as a premiss; in the contrary case, it is said to be empirical. A few words are necessary to make the distinction clear. There is a process by which we acquire knowledge of dated events at times closely contiguous to them; this is the process called "perception" or "introspection"[1] according to the character of the events concerned. There is no doubt need of much discussion as to the nature of this process, and of still more as to the nature of the knowledge to be derived from it; but there can be no doubt of the broad fact that we do acquire knowledge in this way. We wake up and find that it is daylight, or that it is still night; we hear a clock strike; we see a shooting star; we read the newspaper; and so on. In all these cases we acquire knowledge of events, and the time at which we acquire the knowledge is the same, or nearly the same, as that at which the events take place. I shall call this process "perception," and shall, for convenience, include introspection —if this is really different from what is commonly called "perception." A fact of "experience" is one which we could not have known without the help of perception. But this is not quite clear until he have defined what we mean by "could not"; for clearly we may learn from experience that $2 + 2 = 4$, though we afterwards realize that the experience was not logically indispensable. In such cases, we see afterwards that the experience did not prove the proposition, but merely suggested it, and led to our finding the real proof. But, in view of the fact that the distinction between empirical and *a priori* is epistemological, not logical, it is obviously possible for a proposition to change

[1] I do not wish to prejudice the question whether there is such a process as "introspection," but only to include it *if* it exists.

from the one class to the other, since the classification involves reference to the organization of a particular person's knowledge at a particular time. So regarded, the distinction might seem unimportant; but it suggests some less subjective distinctions, which are what we really wish to consider.

Kant's philosophy started from the question: How are synthetic *a priori* judgments possible? Now we must first of all make a distinction. Kant is concerned with *knowledge*, not with mere *belief*. There is no philosophical problem in the fact that a man can have a *belief* which is synthetic and not based on experience—e.g. that this time the horse on which he has put his money will win. The philosophical problem arises only if there is a class of synthetic *a priori* beliefs which is always true. Kant considered the propositions of pure mathematics to be of this kind; but in this he was misled by the common opinion of his time, to the effect that geometry, though a branch of pure mathematics, gave information about actual space. Owing to non-Euclidean geometry, particularly as applied in the theory of relativity, we must now distinguish sharply between the geometry applicable to actual space, which is an empirical study forming part of physics, and the geometry of pure mathematics, which gives no information as to actual space. Consequently this instance of synthetic *a priori* knowledge, upon which Kant relied, is no longer available. Other kinds have been supposed to exist—for example, ethical knowledge, and the law of causality; but it is not necessary for our purposes to decide whether these kinds really exist or not. So far as physics is concerned, we may assume that all real knowledge is either dependent (at least in part) upon perception, or analytic in the sense in which pure mathematics is analytic. The Kantian synthetic *a priori* knowledge, whether it exists or not, seems not to be found in physics—unless, indeed, the principle of induction were to count as such.

But the principle of induction . . . has its origin in physiology, and this suggests a quite different treatment of *a priori* beliefs from that of Kant. Whether there is *a priori knowledge* or not, there undoubtedly are, in a certain sense, *a priori beliefs*. We have reflexes which we intellectualize into beliefs; we blink, and this leads us to the belief that an object touching the eye will hurt it. We may have this belief before we have experience of its truth; if so, it is, in a sense, synthetic *a priori* knowledge— i.e. it is a belief, not based upon experience, in a true synthetic proposition. Our belief in induction is essentially analogous. But such beliefs, even when true, hardly deserve to be called knowledge, since they are not all true, and therefore all require verification before they ought to be regarded as certain. These beliefs have been useful in generating science, since they supplied hypotheses which were largely true; but they need not survive untested in modern science.

I shall therefore assume that, at any rate in every department relevant to physics, all knowledge is either analytic in the sense in which logic and pure mathematics are analytic, or is, at least in part, derived from perception. And all knowledge which is in any degree necessarily dependent upon perception I shall call "empirical." I shall regard a piece of knowledge as necessarily dependent upon perception when, after a careful analysis of our grounds for believing it, it is found that among these grounds there is the cognition of an event in time, arising at the same time as the event or very shortly after it, and fulfilling certain further criteria which are necessary in order to distinguish perception from certain kinds of error. . . .

In a science, there are two kinds of empirical propositions. There are those concerned with particular matters of fact, and those concerned with laws induced from matters of fact. The appearances presented by the sun and moon and planets on certain occasions when they have been seen are particular matters of fact. The inference that the sun and moon and planets exist even when no one is observing them—in particular, that the sun exists at night and the planets by day—is an empirical induction. Heraclitus thought the sun was new every day, and there was no logical impossibility in this hypothesis. Thus empirical laws not only depend upon particular matters of fact, but are inferred from these by a process which falls short of logical demonstration. They differ from propositions of pure mathematics both through the nature of their premisses and through the method by which they are inferred from these premisses.

In an advanced science such as physics, the part played by pure mathematics consists in connecting various empirical generalizations with each other, so that the more general laws which replace them are based upon a larger number of matters of fact. The passage from Kepler's laws to the law of gravitation is the stock instance. Each of the three laws was based upon a certain set of facts; all three sets of facts together formed the basis of the law of gravitation. And, as usually happens in such cases, new facts, not belonging to any of the three previous sets, were found to support the new law—for instance, the facts of tides, of lunar motion, and of perturbations. Epistemologically, in such cases, a fact is a premiss for a law; logically, most of the relevant facts are consequences of the law—i.e. all except those required to determine the constants of integration.

In history and geography, the empirical facts are, at present, more important than any generalizations based upon them. In theoretical physics, the opposite is the case: the fact that the sun and the moon exist is chiefly interesting as affording evidence of the law of gravitation and the laws of the transmission of light. In a philosophic analysis of physics, we need not consider particular facts except when they form the evidence for a theory. It is of course part of the business of such an analysis to consider what all particular facts have in common, and how they come to be known; but such inquiries are general. We are interested in the concept of topography, but not in the actual topography of the universe; at least, we are not interested in it for its own sake, but only as affording the evidence for general laws.

CHAPTER TWO

Mathematics and Logic

Mathematics and logic, historically speaking, have been entirely distinct studies. Mathematics has been connected with science, logic with Greek. But both have developed in modern times: logic has become more mathematical and mathematics has become more logical. The consequence is that it has now become wholly impossible to draw a line between the two; in fact, the two are one. They differ as boy and man: logic is the youth of mathematics and mathematics is the manhood of logic. This view is resented by logicians who, having spent their time in the study of classical texts, are incapable of following a piece of symbolic reasoning, and by mathematicians who have learnt a technique without troubling to inquire into its meaning or justification. Both types are now fortunately growing rarer. So much of modern mathematical work is obviously on the border-line of logic, so much of modern logic is symbolic and formal, that the very close relationship of logic and mathematics has become obvious to every instructed student. The proof of their identity is, of course, a matter of detail: starting with premises which would be universally admitted to belong to logic, and arriving by deduction at results which as obviously belong to mathematics, we find that there is no point at which a sharp line can be drawn, with logic to the left and mathematics to the right. If there are still those who do not admit the identity of

From *Introduction to Mathematical Philosophy* by Bertrand Russell (1919), Chapter XVIII, pp. 194-206. Reprinted by permission of the publishers, George Allen & Unwin Ltd., London. Russell's references to earlier chapters in the original work have here been retained.

logic and mathematics, we may challenge them to indicate at what point, in the successive definitions and deductions of *Principia Mathematica,* they consider that logic ends and mathematics begins. It will then be obvious that any answer must be quite arbitrary.

In the earlier chapters of this book, starting from the natural numbers, we have first defined "cardinal number" and shown how to generalise the conception of number, and have then analysed the conceptions involved in the definition, until we found ourselves dealing with the fundamentals of logic. In a synthetic, deductive treatment these fundamentals come first, and the natural numbers are only reached after a long journey. Such treatment, though formally more correct than that which we have adopted, is more difficult for the reader, because the ultimate logical concepts and propositions with which it starts are remote and unfamiliar as compared with the natural numbers. Also they represent the present frontier of knowledge, beyond which is the still unknown; and the dominion of knowledge over them is not as yet very secure.

It used to be said that mathematics is the science of "quantity." "Quantity" is a vague word, but for the sake of argument we may replace it by the word "number." The statement that mathematics is the science of number would be untrue in two different ways. On the one hand, there are recognised branches of mathematics which have nothing to do with number—all geometry that does not use co-ordinates or measurement, for example: projective and descriptive geometry, down to the point at which co-ordinates are introduced, does not have to do with number, or even with quantity in the sense of *greater* and *less.* On the other hand, through the definition of cardinals, through the theory of induction and ancestral relations, through the general theory of series, and through the definitions of the arithmetical operations, it has become possible to generalise much that used to be proved only in connection with numbers. The result is that what was formerly the single study of Arithmetic has now become divided into numbers of separate studies, no one of which is specially concerned with numbers. The most elementary properties of numbers are concerned with one-one relations, and similarity between classes. Addition is concerned with the construction of mutually exclusive classes respectively similar to a set of classes which are not known to be mutually exclusive. Multiplication is merged in the theory of "selections," i.e. of a certain kind of one-many relations. Finitude is merged in the general study of ancestral relations, which yields the whole theory of mathematical induction. The ordinal properties of the various kinds of number-series, and the elements of the theory of continuity of functions and the limits of functions, can be generalised so as no longer to involve any essential reference to numbers. It is a principle, in all formal reasoning, to generalize to the utmost, since we thereby secure that a given process of deduction shall have more widely applicable results; we are, therefore, in thus generalising the reasoning of arithmetic, merely following a precept which is universally admitted in mathematics. And in thus generalising we have, in effect, created a set of new deductive systems, in which traditional arithmetic is at once dissolved and enlarged; but whether any one of these new deductive systems—for example, the theory of selections—is to be said to belong to logic or to arithmetic is entirely arbitrary, and incapable of being decided rationally.

We are thus brought face to face with the question: What is this subject, which may be called indifferently either mathematics or logic? Is there any way in which we can define it?

Certain characteristics of the subject are clear. To begin with, we do not, in this subject, deal with particular things or particular properties: we deal formally with what can be said about *any* thing or *any* property. We are prepared to say that one and one are two, but not that Socrates and Plato are two, because, in our capacity of logicians or pure mathematicians, we have never heard of Socrates and Plato. A world in which there were no such individuals would still be a world in which one and one are two. It is not open to us, as pure mathematicians or logicians, to mention anything at all, because, if we do so, we introduce something irrelevant and not formal. We may make this clear by applying it to the case of the syllogism. Traditional logic says: "All men are mortal, Socrates is a man, therefore Socrates is mortal." Now it is clear that what we *mean* to assert, to begin with, is only that the premisses imply the conclusion, not that premisses and conclusion are actually true; even the most traditional logic points out that the actual truth of the premisses is irrelevant to logic. Thus the first change to be made in the above traditional syllogism is to state it in the form: "If all men are mortal and Socrates is a man, then Socrates is mortal." We may now observe that it is intended to convey that this argument is valid in virtue of its *form,* not in virtue of the particular terms occurring in it. If we had omitted "Socrates is a man" from our premisses, we should have had a non-formal argument, only admissible because Socrates is in fact a man; in that case we could not have generalised the argument. But when, as above, the argument is *formal,* nothing depends upon the terms that occur in it. Thus we may substitute α for *men,* β for *mortals,* and x for Socrates, where α and β are any classes whatever, and x is any individual. We then arrive at the statement: "No matter what possible values x and α and β may have, if all α's are β's and x is an α, then x is a β"; in other words, "the propositional function 'if all α's are β and x is an α, then x is a β' is always true." Here at last we have a proposition of logic—the one which is only *suggested* by the traditional statement about Socrates and men and mortals.

It is clear that, if *formal* reasoning is what we are aiming at, we shall always arrive ultimately at statements like the above, in which no actual things or properties are mentioned; this will happen through the mere desire not to waste our time proving in a particular case what can be proved generally. It would be ridiculous to go through a long argument about Socrates, and then go through precisely the same argument again about Plato. If our argument is one (say) which holds of all men, we shall prove it concerning "x," with the hypothesis "if x is a man." With this hypothesis, the argument will retain its hypothetical validity even when x is not a man. But now we shall find that our argument would still be valid if, instead of supposing x to be a man, we were to suppose him to be a monkey or a goose or a Prime Minister. We shall therefore not waste our time taking as our premiss "x is a man" but shall take "x is an a," where a is any class of individuals, or "ϕx" where ϕ is any propositional function of some assigned type. Thus the absence of all mention of particular things or properties in logic or pure mathematics is a necessary result of the fact that this study is, as we say, "purely formal."

At this point we find ourselves faced with a problem which is easier to state than to solve. The problem is: "What are the constituents of a logical proposition?" I do not know the answer, but I propose to explain how the problem arises.

Take (say) the proposition "Socrates was before Aristotle." Here it seems obvious that we have a relation between two terms, and that the constituents of the proposition (as well as of the corresponding fact) are simply the two terms and the relation, i.e. Socrates, Aristotle, and *before*. (I ignore the fact that Socrates and Aristotle are not simple; also the fact that what appear to be their names are really truncated descriptions. Neither of these facts is relevant to the present issue.) We may represent the general form of such propositions by "x R y," which may be read "x has the relation R to y." This general form may occur in logical propositions, but no particular instance of it can occur. Are we to infer that the general form itself is a constituent of such logical propositions?

Given a proposition, such as "Socrates is before Aristotle," we have certain constituents and also a certain form. But the form is not itself a new constituent; if it were, we should need a new form to embrace both it and the other constituents. We can, in fact, turn *all* the constituents of a proposition into variables, while keeping the form unchanged. This is what we do when we use such a schema as "x R y," which stands for any one of a certain class of propositions, namely, those asserting relations between two terms. We can proceed to general assertions, such as "x R y is sometimes true"—i.e. there are cases where dual relations hold. This assertion will belong to logic (or mathematics) in the sense in which we are using the word. But in this assertion we do not mention any particular things or particular relations; no particular things or relations can ever enter into a proposition of pure logic. We are left with pure *forms* as the only possible constituents of logical propositions.

I do not wish to assert positively that pure forms—e.g. the form "$x \, R \, y$"—do actually enter into propositions of the kind we are considering. The question of the analysis of such propositions is a difficult one, with conflicting considerations on the one side and on the other. We cannot embark upon this question now, but we may accept, as a first approximation, the view that *forms* are what enter into logical propositions as their constituents. And we may explain (though not formally define) what we mean by the "form" of a proposition as follows:—

The "form" of a proposition is that, in it, that remains unchanged when every constituent of the proposition is replaced by another.

Thus "Socrates is earlier than Aristotle" has the same form as "Napoleon is greater than Wellington," though every constituent of the two propositions is different.

We may thus lay down, as a necessary (though not sufficient) characteristic of logical or mathematical propositions, that they are to be such as can be obtained from a proposition containing no variables (i.e. no such words as *all, some, a, the,* etc.) by turning every constituent into a variable and asserting that the result is always true or sometimes true, or that it is always true in respect of some of the variables that the result is sometimes true in respect of the others, or any variant of these forms. And another way of stating the same thing is to say that logic (or mathematics) is concerned only with *forms,* and is concerned with them only in the way of stating that they are always or sometimes true—with all the permutations of "always" and "sometimes" that may occur.

There are in every language some words whose sole function is to indicate form. These words, broadly speaking, are commonest in languages having fewest inflections. Take "Socrates is human." Here "is" is not a constituent of the proposition, but merely indicates the subject-predicate form. Similarly in "Socrates is earlier than Aristotle," "is" and "than" merely indicate form; the proposition is the same as "Socrates precedes Aristotle," in which these words have disappeared and the form is otherwise indicated. Form, as a rule, *can* be indicated otherwise than by specific words: the order of the words can do most of what is wanted. But this principle must not be pressed. For example, it is difficult to see how we could conveniently express molecular forms of propositions (i.e. what we call "truth-functions") without any word at all. We saw in Chapter XIV that one word or symbol is enough for this purpose, namely, a word or symbol expressing *incompatibility*. But without even one we should find ourselves in difficulties. This, however, is not the point that is important for our present purpose. What is important for us is to observe that form may be the one concern of a general proposition, even when no word or symbol in that proposition designates the form. If we wish to speak about the form itself, we must have a word for it; but if, as in mathematics, we wish to speak about all propositions that have the form, a word for the form will usually be found not indispensable; probably in theory it is *never* indispensable.

Assuming—as I think we may—that the forms of propositions *can* be represented by the forms of the propositions in which they are expressed without any special word for forms, we should arrive at a language in which everything formal belonged to syntax and not to vocabulary. In such a language we could express *all* the propositions of mathematics even if we did not know one single word of the language. The language of mathematical logic, if it were perfected, would be such a language. We should have symbols for variables, such as "x" and "R" and "y," arranged in various ways; and the way of arrangement would indicate that something was being said to be true of all values or some values of the variables. We should not need to know any words, because they would only be needed for giving values to the variables, which is the business of the applied mathematician, not of the pure mathematician or logician. It is one of the marks of a proposition of logic that, given a suitable language, such a proposition can be asserted in such a language

by a person who knows the syntax without knowing a single
word of the vocabulary.

But, after all, there are words that express form, such as "is"
and "than." And in every symbolism hitherto invented for
mathematical logic there are symbols having constant formal
meanings. We may take as an example the symbol for incompatibility which is employed in building up truth-functions.
Such words or symbols may occur in logic. The question is:
How are we to define them?

Such words or symbols express what are called "logical constants." Logical constants may be defined exactly as we defined
forms; in fact, they are in essence the same thing. A fundamental
logical constant will be that which is in common among a number of propositions, any one of which can result from any other
by substitution of terms one for another. For example, "Napoleon is greater than Wellington" results from "Socrates is earlier
than Aristotle" by the substitution of "Napoleon" for "Socrates," "Wellington" for "Aristotle," and "greater" for "earlier."
Some propositions can be obtained in this way from the prototype "Socrates is earlier than Aristotle" and some cannot; those
that can are those that are of the form "$x \ R \ y$," i.e. express dual
relations. We cannot obtain from the above prototype by term-for-term substitution such propositions as "Socrates is human"
or "the Athenians gave the hemlock to Socrates," because the
first is of the subject-predicate form and the second expresses
a three-term relation. If we are to have any words in our pure
logical language, they must be such as express "logical constants," and "logical constants" will always either be, or be derived from, what is in common among a group of propositions
derivable from each other, in the above manner, by term-for-term substitution. And this which is in common is what we call
"form."

In this sense all the "constants" that occur in pure mathematics are logical constants. The number 1, for example, is
derivative from propositions of the form: "There is a term c
such that ϕx is true when, and only when, x is c." This is a
function of ϕ, and various different propositions result from

giving different values to ϕ. We may (with a little omission of intermediate steps not relevant to our present purpose) take the above function of ϕ as what is meant by "the class determined by ϕ is a unit class" or "the class determined by ϕ is a member of 1" (1 being a class of classes). In this way, propositions in which 1 occurs acquire a meaning which is derived from a certain constant logical form. And the same will be found to be the case with all mathematical constants: all are logical constants, or symbolic abbreviations whose full use in a proper context is defined by means of logical constants.

But although all logical (or mathematical) propositions can be expressed wholly in terms of logical constants together with variables, it is not the case that, conversely, all propositions that can be expressed in this way are logical. We have found so far a necessary but not a sufficient criterion of mathematical propositions. We have sufficiently defined the character of the primitive *ideas* in terms of which all the ideas of mathematics can be *defined*, but not of the primitive *propositions* from which all the propositions of mathematics can be *deduced*. This is a more difficult matter, as to which it is not yet known what the full answer is.

We may take the axiom of infinity as an example of a proposition which, though it can be enunciated in logical terms, cannot be asserted by logic to be true. All the propositions of logic have a characteristic which used to be expressed by saying that they were analytic, or that their contradictories were self-contradictory. This mode of statement, however, is not satisfactory. The law of contradiction is merely one among logical propositions; it has no special pre-eminence; and the proof that the contradictory of some proposition is self-contradictory is likely to require other principles of deduction besides the law of contradiction. Nevertheless, the characteristic of logical propositions that we are in search of is the one which was felt, and intended to be defined, by those who said that it consisted in deducibility from the law of contradiction. This characteristic, which, for the moment, we may call *tautology*, obviously does not belong to the assertion that the number of individuals in the universe is n, whatever number n may be. But for the diversity of types, it would be possible to prove logically that there are classes of n terms, where n is any finite integer; or even that there are classes of $\aleph_0$ terms. But, owing to types, such proofs, as we saw in Chapter XIII, are fallacious. We are left to empirical observation to determine whether there are as many as n individuals in the world. Among "possible" worlds, in the Leibnizian sense, there will be worlds having one, two, three, . . . individuals. There does not even seem any logical necessity why there should be even one individual[1]—why, in fact, there should be any world at all. The ontological proof of the existence of God, if it were valid, would establish the logical necessity of at least one individual. But it is generally recognized as invalid, and in fact rests upon a mistaken view of existence—i.e. it fails to realise that existence can only be asserted of something described, not of something named, so that it is meaningless to argue from "this is the so-and-so" and "the so-and-so exists" to "this exists." If we reject the ontological argument, we seem driven to conclude that the existence of a world is an accident— i.e. it is not logically necessary. If that be so, no principle of logic can assert "existence" except under a hypothesis, i.e. none can be of the form "the propositional function so-and-so is sometimes true." Propositions of this form, when they occur in logic, will have to occur as hypotheses or consequences of hypotheses, not as complete asserted propositions. The complete asserted propositions of logic will all be such as affirm that some propositional function is *always* true. For example, it is always true that if p implies q and q implies r then p implies r, or that, if all α's are β's and x is an α then x is a β. Such propositions may occur in logic, and their truth is independent of the existence of the universe. We may lay it down that, if there were no universe, *all* general propositions would be true; for the contradictory of a general proposition (as we saw in Chapter XV) is a proposition asserting existence, and would therefore always be false if no universe existed.

[1] The primitive propositions in *Principia Mathematica* are such as to allow the inference that at least one individual exists. But I now view this as a defect in logical purity.

Logical propositions are such as can be known *a priori,* without study of the actual world. We only know from a study of empirical facts that Socrates is a man, but we know the correctness of the syllogism in its abstract form (i.e. when it is stated in terms of variables) without needing any appeal to experience. This is a characteristic, not of logical propositions in themselves, but of the way in which we know them. It has, however, a bearing upon the question what their nature may be, since there are some kinds of propositions which it would be very difficult to suppose we could know without experience.

It is clear that the definition of "logic" or "mathematics" must be sought by trying to give a new definition of the old notion of "analytic" propositions. Although we can no longer be satisfied to define logical propositions as those that follow from the law of contradiction, we can and must still admit that they are a wholly different class of propositions from those that we come to know empirically. They all have the characteristic which, a moment ago, we agreed to call "tautology." This, combined with the fact that they can be expressed wholly in terms of variables and logical constants (a logical constant being something which remains constant in a proposition even when *all* its constituents are changed)—will give the definition of logic or pure mathematics. For the moment, I do not know how to define "tautology."[1] It would be easy to offer a definition which might seem satisfactory for a while; but I know of none that I feel to be satisfactory, in spite of feeling thoroughly familiar with the characteristic of which a definition is wanted. At this point, therefore, for the moment, we reach the frontier of knowledge on our backward journey into the logical foundations of mathematics.

We have now come to an end of our somewhat summary introduction to mathematical philosophy. It is impossible to convey adequately the ideas that are concerned in this subject so long as we abstain from the use of logical symbols. Since ordi-

[1] The importance of "tautology" for a definition of mathematics was pointed out to me by my former pupil Ludwig Wittgenstein, who was working on the problem. I do not know whether he has solved it, or even whether he is alive or dead.

nary language has no words that naturally express exactly what we wish to express, it is necessary, so long as we adhere to ordinary language, to strain words into unusual meanings; and the reader is sure, after a time if not at first, to lapse into attaching the usual meanings to words, thus arriving at wrong notions as to what is intended to be said. Moreover, ordinary grammar and syntax is extraordinarily misleading. This is the case, e.g., as regards numbers; "ten men" is grammatically the same form as "white men," so that 10 might be thought to be an adjective qualifying "men." It is the case, again, wherever propositional functions are involved, and in particular as regards existence and descriptions. Because language is misleading, as well as because it is diffuse and inexact when applied to logic (for which it was never intended), logical symbolism is absolutely necessary to any exact or thorough treatment of our subject. Those readers, therefore, who wish to acquire a mastery of the principles of mathematics, will, it is to be hoped, not shrink from the labour of mastering the symbols—a labour which is, in fact, much less than might be thought.

CHAPTER THREE

Interpretation

The matter with which we are now to be concerned is *interpreta-ation*. It often happens that we have what seems adequate reason to believe in the truth of some formula expressed in mathematical symbols, although we are not in a position to give a clear definition of the symbols. It happens also, in other cases, that we can give a number of different meanings to the symbols, all of which will make the formula true. In the former case we lack even one definite interpretation of our formula, whereas in the latter we have many. This situation, which may seem odd, arises in pure mathematics and in mathematical physics; it arises even in interpreting common-sense statements such as "My room contains three tables and four chairs." It will thus appear that there is a large class of statements, concerning each of which in some sense we are more certain of its truth than of its meaning. "Interpretation" is concerned with such statements; it consists in finding as precise a meaning as possible for a statement of this sort, or, sometimes, in finding a whole system of possible meanings.

Let us take first an illustration from pure mathematics. Mankind have long been convinced that $2 + 2 = 4$; they have been so firmly convinced of this that it has been taken as the stock example of something certain. But when people were asked

what they meant by "2," "4," "+," and "=," they gave vague
and divergent answers, which made it plain that they did not
know what these symbols meant. Some maintained that we
know each of the numbers by intuition, and therefore have no
need to define them. This might seem fairly plausible where
small numbers were concerned, but who could have an intuition of 3,478,921? So they said we had an intuition of "1" and
"+"; we could then define "2" as "1 + 1," "3" as "2 + 1,"
"4" as "3 + 1," and so on. But this did not work very well. It
enabled us to say that 2 + 2 = (1 + 1) + (1 + 1) and that 4 =
{(1 + 1) + 1} + 1, and we then needed a fresh intuition to
tell us that we could rearrange the brackets, in fact to assure
us that if l, m, n are three numbers, then $(l + m) + n = l +
(m + n)$. Some philosophers were able to produce this intuition
on demand, but most people remained somewhat skeptical of
their claims, and felt that some other method was called for.

A new development, more germane to our problem of interpretation, was due to Peano. Peano started with three undefined
terms—"0," "finite integer (or number)," and "successor of"—
and concerning these terms he made five assumptions, namely:

1. 0 is a number;
2. If a is a number, the successor of a (i.e., $a + 1$) is a number;
3. If two numbers have the same successor, the two numbers
   are identical;
4. 0 is not the successor of any number;
5. If s be a class to which belongs 0 and also the successor of
   every number belonging to s, then every number belongs
   to s.

The last of these assumptions is the principle of mathematical
induction.

Peano showed that by means of these five assumptions he
could prove every formula in arithmetic.

But now a new trouble arose. It was assumed that we need not
know what we meant by "0," "number," and "successor," so
long as we meant something satisfying the five assumptions. But
then it turned out that there were an infinite number of possible
interpretations. For instance, let "0" mean what we commonly

call "1," and let "number" mean what we commonly call "number other than 0"; then all the five assumptions are still true, and all arithmetic can be proved, though every formula will have an unexpected meaning. "2" will mean what we usually call "3," but "2 + 2" will not mean "3 + 3"; it will mean "3 + 2," and "2 + 2 = 4" will mean what we usually express by "3 + 2 = 5." In like manner we could interpret arithmetic on the assumption that "0" means "100," and "number" means "number greater than 99." And so on.

So long as we remain in the region of arithmetical formulas, all these different interpretations of "number" are equally good. It is only when we come to the empirical uses of numbers in enumeration that we find a reason for preferring one interpretation to all the others. When we buy something in a shop and the attendant says, "Three shillings, please," his "three" is not a mere mathematical symbol, meaning "the third term after the beginning of some series"; his "three," in fact, is not capable of being defined by its *arithmetical* properties. It is obvious that his interpretation of "three" is, outside arithmetic, preferable to all the others that Peano's system leaves possible. Such statements as "Men have 10 fingers," "Dogs have 4 legs," "New York has 10,000,000 inhabitants" require a definition of numbers which cannot be derived from the mere fact that they satisfy the formulas of arithmetic. Such a definition is, therefore, the most satisfactory "interpretation" of number-symbols.

The same sort of situation arises whenever mathematics is applied to empirical material. Take, for example, geometry, considered not as a logical exercise in deducing consequences from arbitrarily assumed axioms but as a help in land-surveying, map-making, engineering, or astronomy. Such practical uses of geometry involve a difficulty which, though sometimes admitted in a perfunctory manner, is never allowed anything like its due weight. Geometry, as set forth by the mathematicians, uses points, lines, planes, and circles, but it is a platitude to say that no such objects are to be found in nature. When, in surveying, we use the process of triangulation, it is admitted that our triangles do not have accurate straight lines for their

sides nor exact points at their corners, but this is glozed over
by saying that the sides are *approximately* straight and the
corners *approximately* points. It is not at all clear what this
means, so long as it is maintained that there are no exact straight
lines or points to which our rough-and-ready lines and points
approximate. We may mean that sensible lines and points have
approximately the properties set forth by Euclid, but unless
we can say, within limits, how close the approximation is, such
a view will make calculation vague and unsatisfactory.

This problem of the exactness of mathematics and the in-
exactness of sense is an ancient one, which Plato solved by the
fantastic hypothesis of reminiscence. In modern times, like some
other unsolved problems, it has been forgotten through fam-
iliarity, like a bad smell which you no longer notice because
you have lived with it so long. It is clear that if geometry is to
be applied to the sensible world, we must be able to find definitions of points, lines, planes, etc., in terms of sensible data, or
else we must be able to infer from sensible data the existence
of unperceived entities having the properties that geometry
needs. To find ways, or a way, of doing one or other of these
things is the problem of the empirical interpretation of
geometry.

There is also a non-empirical interpretation, which leaves
geometry within the sphere of pure mathematics. The assemblage of all ordered triads of real numbers forms a three-dimensional Euclidean space. With this interpretation, all Euclidean
geometry is deducible from arithmetic. Every non-Euclidean
geometry is capable of a similar arithmetical interpretation. It
can be proved that Euclidean geometry, and every form of non-
Euclidean geometry, can be applied to every class having the
same number of terms as the real numbers; the question of
the number of dimensions, and whether the resulting geometry
is Euclidean or non-Euclidean, will depend upon the ordering
relation that we select; an infinite number of ordering relations
exists (in the logical sense), and only reasons of empirical convenience can lead us to select some one among them for special
attention. All this is relevant in considering what interpretation

of pure geometry had better be adopted by the engineer or the physicist. It shows that, in an empirical interpretation, the ordering relation, and not only the terms ordered, must be defined in empirical terms.

Very similar considerations apply to time, which, however, so far as our present question is concerned, is not so difficult a problem as space. In mathematical physics, time is treated as consisting of instants, though the perplexed student is assured that instants are mathematical fictions. No attempt is made to show him why fictions are useful, or how they are related to what is not fictitious. He finds that by the use of these fairy tales it is possible to calculate what really happens, and after a time he probably ceases to trouble himself as to why this is the case.

Instants were not always regarded as fictions; Newton thought them as "real" as the sun and moon. When this view was abandoned, it was easy to swing to the opposite extreme, and to forget that a fiction which is useful is not likely to be a *mere* fiction. There are degrees of fictiveness. Let us, for the moment, regard an individual person as something in no degree fictive; what, then, shall we say of the various aggregates of persons to which he belongs? Most people would hesitate to regard a family as a fictitious unit, but what about a political party or a cricket club? What about the assemblage of persons called "Smith," to which we will suppose our individual to belong? If you believe in astrology, you will attach importance to the assemblage of persons born under a certain planet; if you do not, you will regard such an assemblage as fictive. These distinctions are not logical; from the logical point of view, all assemblages of individuals are equally real or equally fictive. The importance of the distinctions is practical, not logical: there are some assemblages about which there are many useful things to be said, and others about which this is not the case.

When we say that instants are useful fictions, we must be supposed to mean that there are entities to which, as to individual people, we feel inclined to attach a high degree of "reality" (whatever that may mean), and that, in comparison with them, instants have that lesser degree of "reality" that cricket clubs have in relation to their members; but we wish also to say that about instants, as about families as opposed to "artificial" aggregates of people, there are many practically important things to say.

All this is very vague, and the problem of interpretation is that of substituting something precise, remembering always that however we define "instants," they must have the properties required in mathematical physics. Given two interpretations which both satisfy this requisite, the choice between them is one of taste and convenience; there is not one interpretation which is "right" and others that are "wrong."

In classical physics, the technical apparatus consists of points, instants, and particles. It is assumed that there is a three-term relation, that of occupying a point at an instant, and what occupies a point at an instant is called a "particle." It is also assumed technically that particles are indestructible, so that whatever occupies a point at a given instant occupies *some* point at every other instant. When I say that this is assumed, I do not mean that it is asserted to be a fact, but that the technique is based on the assumption that no harm will come of treating it as a fact. This is still held to be the case in macroscopic physics, but in microscopic physics "particles" have been gradually disappearing. "Matter" in the old sense is no longer needed; what is needed is "energy," which is not defined except as regards its laws and the relation of changes in its distribution to our sensations, more especially the relation of frequencies to color perceptions.

Broadly speaking, we may say that the fundamental technical apparatus of modern physics is a four-dimensional manifold of "events" ordered by space-time relations, which can be analyzed into a spatial and a temporal component in a number of ways, the choice between which is arbitrary. Since the calculus is still used, it is still technically assumed that space-time is continuous, but it is not clear how far this assumption is more than a mathematical convenience. Nor is it clear that "events" have that precise location in space-time that used to characterize a particle at an instant. All this makes the question of the interpretation of modern physics very difficult, but in the absence of *some* interpretation we cannot say what is being asserted by the quantum physicists.

"Interpretation," in its logical aspect, is somewhat different from the rather vague and difficult concept which we considered at the beginning of this chapter. We were there concerned with symbolic statements which are known to have a connection with observable phenomena, and to lead to results which observation confirms, but are somewhat indeterminate in meaning except in so far as their connection with observation defines them. In this case we can say, as we said at the beginning of this chapter, that we are pretty sure our formulas are true, but not at all sure what they mean. In logic, however, we proceed differently. Our formulas are not regarded as "true" or "false," but as hypotheses containing variables. A set of values of the variables which makes the hypotheses true is an "interpretation." The word "point," in geometry, may be interpreted as meaning "ordered triad of real numbers," or, as we shall see, as meaning what we shall call "complete complex of compresence"; it may also be interpreted in an infinite number of other ways. What all the ways have in common is that they satisfy the axioms of geometry.

We often have, both in pure and applied mathematics, collections of formulas all logically deducible from a small number of initial formulas, which may be called "axioms." These axioms may be regarded as hostages for the whole system, and we may concentrate our attention exclusively upon them. The axioms consist partly of terms having a known definition, partly of terms which, in any interpretation, will remain variables, and partly of terms which, though as yet undefined, are intended to acquire definitions when the axioms are "interpreted." The process of interpretation consists in finding a constant signification for this class of terms. The signification may be given by a verbal definition, or may be given otensively. It must be such that, with this interpretation, the axioms become *true*. (Before interpretation, they are neither true nor false.) It thus follows that all their consequences are also true.

Suppose, for example, we wish to interpret the formulas of arithmetic. In Peano's five axioms (given above) there are: first, logical terms, such as "is a" and "is identical with," of which the meaning is supposed known; second, variables, such as a and s, which are to remain variables after interpretation; third, the terms "o" "number," and "successor of," for which an interpretation is to find a constant meaning which makes the five axioms true. As we saw, there are an infinite number of interpretations satisfying these conditions, but there is only one among them which also satisfies empirical statements of enumeration, such as "I have 10 fingers." In this case, therefore, there is one interpretation which is very much more convenient than any of the others.

As we saw in the case of geometry, a given set of axioms may be capable of two sorts of interpretation, one logical and one empirical. All nominal definitions, if pushed back far enough, must lead ultimately to terms having only ostensive definitions, and in the case of an empirical science the empirical terms must depend upon terms of which the ostensive definition is given in perception. The astronomer's sun, for instance, is very different from what we see, but it must have a definition derived from the ostensive definition of the word "sun" which we learned in childhood. Thus an empirical interpretation of a set of axioms, when complete, must always involve the use of terms which have an ostensive definition derived from sensible experience. It will not, of course, contain *only* such terms, for there will always also be logical terms; but it is the presence of terms derived from experience that makes an interpretation empirical.

The question of interpretation has been unduly neglected. So long as we remain in the region of mathematical formulas, everything appears precise, but when we seek to interpret them it turns out that the precision is partly illusory. Until this matter has been cleared up, we cannot tell with any exactitude what any given science is asserting.

CHAPTER FOUR

Minimum Vocabularies

In the present chapter we shall be concerned with a linguistic technique which is very useful in the analysis of scientific concepts. There are as a rule a number of ways in which the words used in a science can be defined in terms of a few among them. These few may have ostensive definitions, or may have nominal definitions in terms of words not belonging to the science in question, or—so long as the science is not "interpreted" in the sense considered in the last chapter—they may be left without either ostensive or nominal definition, and regarded merely as a set of terms having the properties which the science ascribes to its fundamental terms. Such a set of initial words I call a "minimum vocabulary" for the science in question, provided that (a) every other word used in the science has a nominal definition in terms of these words, and (b) no one of these initial words has a nominal definition in terms of the other initial words.

Everything said in a science can be said by means of the words in a minimum vocabulary. For whenever a word occurs which has a nominal definition, we can substitute the defining phrase; if this contains words with a nominal definition, we can again substitute the defining phrase, and so on, until none of the remaining words have nominal definitions. In fact, definable terms are superfluous, and only undefined terms are indispensable. But the question which terms are to be undefined is in part arbitrary. Take, for example, the calculus of propositions, which is the simplest and most completed example of a formal system. We can take "or" and "not" as undefined, or "and" and "not"; instead of two such undefined terms, we can take one, which may be "not this or not that" or "not this and not that." Thus in general we cannot say that such-and-such a word *must* belong to the minimum vocabulary of such-and-such a science, but at most that there are one or more minimum vocabularies to which it belongs.

Let us take geography as an example. I shall assume the vocabulary of geometry already established; then our first distinctively geographical need is a method of assigning latitude and longitude. For this it will suffice to have as part of our minimum vocabulary "Greenwich," "the North Pole," and "west of"; but clearly any other place would do as well as Greenwich, and the South Pole would do as well as the North Pole. The relation "west of" is not really necessary, for a parallel of latitude is a circle on the earth's surface in a plane perpendicular to the diameter passing through the North Pole. The remainder of the words used in physical geography, such as "land" and "water," "mountain" and "plain," can now be defined in terms of chemistry, physics, or geometry. Thus it would seem that it is the two words "Greenwich" and "North Pole" that are needed in order to make geography a science concerning the surface of the earth, and not some other spheroid. It is owing to the presence of these two words (or two others serving the same purpose) that geography is able to relate the discoveries of travelers. It is to be observed that these two words are involved wherever latitude and longitude are mentioned.

As this example illustrates, a science is apt to acquire a smaller minimum vocabulary as it becomes more systematic. The ancients knew many geographical facts before they knew how to assign latitudes and longitudes, but to express these facts they needed a larger number of undefined words than we need. Since the earth is a spheroid, not a sphere, "North Pole" need not be undefined: we can define the two Poles as the extremities of the earth's shortest diameter, and the North Pole as the Pole nearer to Greenwich. In this way we can manage with "Greenwich" as the only undefined term peculiar to geography. The earth itself is defined as "that spheroid whose surface is formed of land and water bounded by air, and on whose surface Greenwich is situated." But here we seem to reach a dead end in the way of diminishing our minimum vocabulary: if we are to be sure that we are talking about the earth, we must mention some place on its surface or having a given geometrical relation to it, and the place must be one which we can recognize. Therefore although "New York" or "Moscow" or "Timbuktu" would do just as well as "Greenwich," *some* place must be included in any minimum vocabulary for geography.

One further point is illustrated by our discussion of Greenwich, and that is that the terms which are officially undefined in a science may not be identical with those that are undefined for a given person. If you have never seen Greenwich, the word "Greenwich" cannot, for you, have an ostensive definition; therefore you cannot understand the word unless it has a nominal definition. In fact, if you live in a place called "P," then for you P takes the place of Greenwich, and your official longitude, for you, defines the meridian of Greenwich, not the longitude of P. Such considerations, however, are pre-scientific, and are usually ignored in the analysis of scientific concepts. For certain purposes, they cannot be ignored, particularly when we are considering the relation of science to sensible experience; but as a rule there is little danger in ignoring them.

Let us consider next the question of minimum vocabularies for astronomy. Astronomy consists of two parts, one a kind of cosmic geography, the other an application of physics. Statements as to the size and orbits of the planets belong to cosmic geography, whereas Newton's and Einstein's theories of gravitation belong to physics. The difference is that in the geographical part we are concerned with statements of fact as to what is where, while in the part which is physics we are concerned with laws. As I shall presently be considering physics on its own account, let us consider first the geographical part of astronomy. In this part, so long as it is in an elementary stage, we need proper names for the sun, the moon, the planets, and all the stars and nebulae. The number of proper names required can, however, be steadily reduced as the science of astronomy advances. "Mercury" can be defined as meaning "the planet nearest the sun," "Venus" as "the second planet," "the earth" as "the third planet," and so on. Constellations are defined by their co-ordinates, and the several stars in a constellation by their order of brightness.

On this system, "the sun" will remain part of our minimum vocabulary, and we shall need what is necessary for defining celestial co-ordinates. "The Pole Star" will not be necessary, since it may be defined as "the star without diurnal revolution," but we shall need some other heavenly body to fulfill the function which Greenwich fulfills in terrestrial geography. In this way official astronomy could get on with (it would seem) only two proper names, "the sun" and, say, "Sirius." "The moon," for instance, can be defined as "the body whose co-ordinates on such-and-such a date are so-and-so." With this vocabulary we can, in a sense, state everything that the astronomer wishes to say, just as, with Peano's three undefined terms, we can state all arithmetic.

But just as Peano's system proves inadequate when we come to counting, so our official astronomy proves inadequate when we attempt to link it to observation. There are two essential propositions which it fails to include, namely, "That is the sun" and "That is Sirius." We have, it appears, formed a vocabulary for astronomy in the abstract, but not for astronomy as a record of observations.

Plato, who was interested in astronomy solely as a body of laws, wished it to be wholly divorced from sense; those who were interested in the actual heavenly bodies that happen to exist would, he said, be punished in the next incarnation by being birds. This point of view is not nowadays adopted by men of science, but it, or something very like it, is to be found in the works of Carnap and some other logical positivists. They are not, I think, conscious of holding any such opinion, and would vehemently repudiate it; but absorption in words, as opposed to what they mean, has exposed them to Platonic temptation, and led them down strange paths toward perdition, or what an empiricist must consider such. Astronomy is not *merely* a collection of words and sentences; it is a collection of words and sentences chosen, from others that were linguistically just as good, because they described a world connected with sensible experience. So long as sensible experience is ignored, no reason appears for concerning ourselves with a large body having just so many planets at just such distances from it. And the sentences in which sensible experience breaks in are such as "That is the sun."

Every advanced science has two aspects: on the one hand, it consists of a body of propositions interconnected in various ways, and often containing a small selection from which all the others can be deduced; on the other hand, it is an attempt to describe some part or aspect of the universe. In the former aspect, the truth or falsehood of the several propositions is not in question, but only their mutual connections. For example, if gravitation varied directly as the distance, planets (if any) would revolve round the sun (if it existed) in ellipses of which the sun would occupy the center, not a focus. This proposition is not part of descriptive astronomy. There is a similar statement, also not part of descriptive astronomy, saying that if gravitation varies inversely as the square of the distance, planets (if any) will go round the sun (if any) in ellipses of which the sun will occupy a focus. This is different from the two statements: Gravitation varies inversely as the square of the distance, and Planets revolve in ellipses round the sun in a focus. The former statement is a hypothetical; the two latter assert both the antecedent and the consequent of the previous hypothetical. What enables them to do this is the appeal to observation.

The appeal to observation is made in statements such as "That is the sun"; such statements, therefore, are essential to the truth of astronomy. Such statements never appear in any finished exposition of an astronomical theory, but they do appear while a theory is being established. For instance, after the eclipse observations in 1919, we were told that the photographs of certain stars appeared with such-and-such a displacement toward the sun. This was a statement as to the positions of certain dots on a photographic plate, as observed by certain astronomers at a certain date; it was a statement not primarily belonging to astronomy, but to biography, and yet it constituted the evidence for an important astronomical theory.

The vocabulary of astronomy, it thus appears, is wider if we consider it as a body of propositions deriving truth, or at least probability, from observation, than it is if we treat it as a purely hypothetical system whose truth or falsehood does not concern us. In the former case we must be able to say, "That is the sun," or something of the sort; in the latter case, no such necessity arises.

Physics, which we must next consider, is in a different position from geography and astronomy, since it is not concerned to say what exists where, but only to establish general laws. "Copper conducts electricity" is a law of physics, but "There is copper in Cornwall" is a fact of geography. The physicist as such does not care where there is copper, so long as there is enough in his laboratory.

In the earlier stages of physics the word "copper" was necessary, but now it has become definable. "Copper" is "the element whose atomic number is 29," and this definition enables us to deduce many things about the copper atom. All the elements can be defined in terms of electrons and protons, or at any rate of electrons, positrons, neutrons, and protons. (Perhaps a proton consists of a neutron and a positron.) These units themselves can be defined by their mass and electric charge. In the last analysis, since mass is a form of energy, it would seem that energy, electric charge, and space-time co-ordinates are all that physics needs; and owing to the absence of the geographical element the co-ordinates can remain purely hypothetical; i.e., there need be no analogue of Greenwich. Physics as a "pure" science—i.e., apart from methods of verification—would seem, therefore, to require only a four-dimensional continuum containing distributions of varying amounts of energy and electricity. Any four-dimensional continuum will do, and "energy" and "electricity" need only be quantities whose mode of change of distribution is subject to certain assigned laws.

When physics is brought to this degree of abstraction it becomes a branch of pure mathematics, which can be pursued without reference to the actual world, and which requires no vocabulary beyond that of pure mathematics. The mathematics, however, are such as no pure mathematician would have thought of for himself. The equations, for instance, contain Planck's constant h, of which the magnitude is about 6.55 $\times$ 10^{-27} erg secs. No one would have thought of introducing just this quantity if there had not been experimental reasons for doing so, and as soon as we introduce experimental reasons the whole picture is changed. The four-dimensional continuum is no longer a mere mathematical hypothesis, but the space-time continuum to which we have been led by successive refinements of the space and time with which we are familiar in experience. Electricity is no longer just any quantity, but the thing measured by the observable behavior of our electrical instruments. Energy, though highly abstract, is a generalization arrived at by means of completely concrete experiments such as those of Joule. Physics as verifiable, therefore, uses various empirical concepts in addition to those purely abstract concepts that are needed in "pure" physics.

Let us consider in more detail the definition of such a term as "energy." The important point about energy is its constancy, and the chief step in establishing its constancy was the determination of the mechanical equivalent of heat. This was effected by observation, for example of thermometers. If, then, we mean by "physics" not merely the body of physical laws, but these together with the evidence for their truth, then we must include in "physics" Joule's perceptions when he looked at thermometers. And what do we mean by "heat"? The plain man means a certain kind of sensation, or its (to him) unknown cause; the physicist means a rapid agitation of the minute parts of bodies. But what has led the physicist to this definition? Only the fact that when we *feel* heat, there is reason to think that such agitation is occurring. Or take the fact that friction causes heat: our primary evidence for this fact is that when we have seen friction we can feel heat. All the non-mathematical terms used in physics considered as an experimental science have their origin in our sensible experience, and it is only on this account that sensible experience can confirm or confute physical laws.

It thus appears that if physics is regarded as a science based on observation, not as a branch of pure mathematics, and if the evidence for physical laws is held to be part of physics, then any minimum vocabulary for physics must be such as to enable us to mention the experiences upon which our physical beliefs are based. We shall need such words as "hot," "red," "hard," not only to describe what physics asserts to be the condition of bodies that give us these sensations but also to describe the sensations themselves. Suppose I say, for instance, "By 'red' light I mean light of such-and-such a range of wave lengths." In that case the statement that light of such wave lengths makes me see red is a tautology, and until the nineteenth century people were uttering meaningless noises when they said that blood is red, because nothing was known of the correlation of wave lengths with sensations of color. This is absurd. It is obvious that "red" has a meaning independent of physics, and that this meaning is relevant in collecting data for the physical theory of colors, just as the pre-scientific meaning of "hot" is relevant in establishing the physical theory of heat.

The main conclusion of the above discussion of minimum vocabularies is that every empirical science, however abstract, must contain in any minimum vocabulary words descriptive of our experiences. Even the most mathematical terms, such as "energy," must, when the chain of definitions is completed until we reach terms of which there is only an ostensive definition, be found to depend for their meaning upon terms directly descriptive of experiences, or even, in what may be called the "geographical" sciences, giving names to particular experiences. This conclusion, if valid, is important, and affords great assistance in the work of interpreting scientific theories.

PART TWO

PART TWO

Sense Data and the Philosophy of Science

Russell's principal problem in the philosophy of science is to determine the relation between experience and the scientific view of the world. In my Introduction I have pointed out that he follows the classical empiricist tradition to the extent of analyzing experience in terms of an individual's 'sense data.' Empirical knowledge is based upon the fragmentary sense data which constitute the individual's immediate perceptual experience. (For the purposes of this book, the terms 'sense datum,' 'percept,' 'appearance,' 'datum' can be used interchangeably.) In his early discussion of the problem, from about 1914 to the early 1920's, he believed that we could interpret, or 'construct,' common-sense objects and scientific entities out of sense data alone, thus relating science and experience. In fact, we could for all practical purposes consider sense data to be the ultimate entities of the world, and common-sense objects and scientific entities to be merely groups of sense data. This view Russell found technically satisfactory; but before long he began to feel it was unconvincing. Part Two consists of an extended development of his early view, while the later one is reserved for Part Three.

Why read his earlier view at all, if he abandoned it? It is valuable for several reasons: (1) it is an interesting view in its own right; (2) this period of Russell's philosophy has had considerable influence on more recent philosophy; and (3) the difficulties Russell found in this view in part determined the direction of his later thought.

CHAPTER ONE

The World of Physics and the
World of Sense

Among the objections to the reality of objects of sense, there is
one which is derived from the apparent difference between matter as it appears in physics and things as they appear in sensation. Men of science, for the most part, are willing to condemn
immediate data as "merely subjective," while yet maintaining
the truth of the physics inferred from those data. But such an
attitude, though it may be *capable* of justification, obviously
stands in need of it; and the only justification possible must be
one which exhibits matter as a logical construction from sense-
data—unless, indeed, there were some wholly *a priori* principle
by which unknown entities could be inferred from such as are
known. It is therefore necessary to find some way of bridging
the gulf between the world of physics and the world of sense,
and it is this problem which will occupy us in the present lecture. Physicists appear to be unconscious of the gulf, while
psychologists, who are conscious of it, have not the mathematical knowledge required for spanning it. The problem is difficult,
and I do not know its solution in detail. All that I can hope to
do is to make the problem felt, and to indicate the kind of
methods by which a solution is to be sought.

Let us begin by a brief description of the two contrasted

From *Our Knowledge of the External World* by Bertrand Russell (2nd edn.,
1929), Lecture IV, pp. 107-137. Reprinted by permission of the publisher,
George Allen & Unwin Ltd., London. The text of this edition is essentially
that of the original edition of 1914.

worlds. We will take first the world of physics, for, though the other world is given while the physical world is inferred, to us now the world of physics is the more familiar, the world of pure sense having become strange and difficult to rediscover. Physics started from the common-sense belief in fairly permanent and fairly rigid bodies—tables and chairs, stones, mountains, the earth and moon and sun. This common-sense belief, it should be noticed, is a piece of audacious metaphysical theorising; objects are not continually present to sensation, and it may be doubted whether they are there when they are not seen or felt. This problem, which has been acute since the time of Berkeley, is ignored by common sense, and has therefore hitherto been ignored by physicists. We have thus here a first departure from the immediate data of sensation, though it is a departure merely by way of extension, and was probably made by our savage ancestors in some very remote prehistoric epoch.

But tables and chairs, stones and mountains, are not *quite* permanent or *quite* rigid. Tables and chairs lose their legs, stones are split by frost, and mountains are cleft by earthquakes and eruptions. Then there are other things, which seem material, and yet present almost no permanence or rigidity. Breath, smoke, clouds are examples of such things—so, in a lesser degree, are ice and snow; and rivers and seas, though fairly permanent, are not in any degree rigid. Breath, smoke, clouds, and generally things that can be seen but not touched, were thought to be hardly real; to this day the usual mark of a ghost is that it can be seen but not touched. Such objects were peculiar in the fact that they seemed to disappear completely, not merely to be transformed into something else. Ice and snow, when they disappear, are replaced by water; and it required no great theoretical effort to invent the hypothesis that the water was the same thing as the ice and snow, but in a new form. Solid bodies, when they break, break into parts which are practically the same in shape and size as they were before. A stone can be hammered into a powder, but the powder consists of grains which retain the character they had before the pounding. Thus the ideal of absolutely rigid and absolutely permanent bodies, which early physicists pursued throughout the changing appearances, seemed attainable by supposing ordinary bodies to be composed of a vast number of tiny atoms. This billiard-ball view of matter dominated the imagination of physicists until quite modern times, until, in fact, it was replaced by the electromagnetic theory, which in its turn developed into a new atomism. Apart from the special form of the atomic theory which was invented for the needs of chemistry, some kind of atomism dominated the whole of traditional dynamics, and was implied in every statement of its laws and axioms.

The pictorial accounts which physicists give of the material world as they conceive it undergo violent changes under the influence of modifications in theory which are much slighter than the layman might suppose from the alterations of the description. Certain features, however, remained fairly stable until the last few years. It was always assumed that there is *something* indestructible which is capable of motion in space; what is indestructible was always very small, but did not always occupy a mere point in space. This view still dominated the Rutherford-Bohr theory of the structure of the atom. Since 1925, however, under the influence of De Broglie, Heisenberg, and Schrödinger, physicists have been led to dissolve the atom into systems of wave-motions, or radiations coming from the place where the atom was supposed to be. This change has brought physics much nearer to psychology, since the supposed permanent material units are now merely logical constructions. In regard to space and time, relativity has introduced a fundamental structural change by merging them in the one four-dimensional space-time. Both these changes have made physics easier to reconcile with psychology than was formerly the case. Both sciences now demand certain departures from common-sense metaphysics, and fortunately the departures they demand harmonize with each other.

Common sense, and physics before the twentieth century, demanded a set of indestructible entities, moving relatively to each other in a single space and a single time. The world of immediate data is quite different from this. Nothing is permanent; even the things that we think are fairly permanent, such as mountains, only become data when we see them, and are not immediately given as existing at other moments. So far from one all-embracing space being given, there are several spaces for each person, according to the different senses which give relations that may be called spatial. Experience teaches us to obtain one space from these by correlation, and experience, together with instinctive theorising, teaches us to correlate our spaces with those which we believe to exist in the sensible worlds of other people. The construction of a single time offers less difficulty so long as we confine ourselves to one person's private world, but relativity has shown that, when we pass beyond one private world, it is space-time, not space and time, that we need. Thus, apart from any of the fluctuating hypotheses of physics, two main problems arise in connecting the world of physics with the world of sense, namely (1) the construction of permanent "things," and (2) the construction of a single space-time. We will consider these two problems in succession.

(1) The belief in indestructible "things" very early took the form of atomism. The underlying motive in atomism was not, I think, any empirical success in interpreting phenomena, but rather an instinctive belief that beneath all the changes of the sensible world there must be something permanent and unchanging. This belief was, no doubt, fostered and nourished by its practical successes, culminating in the conservation of mass; but it was not produced by these successes. On the contrary, they were produced by it. Philosophical writers on physics sometimes speak as though the conservation of something or other were essential to the possibility of science, but this, I believe, is an entirely erroneous opinion. If the *a priori* belief in permanence had not existed, the same laws which are now formulated in terms of this belief might just as well have been formulated without it. Why should we suppose that, when ice melts, the water which replaces it is the same thing in a new form? Merely because this supposition enables us to state the phenomena in a way which is consonant with our prejudices. What we really know is that, under certain conditions of tem-

perature, the appearance we call ice is replaced by the appearance we call water. We can give laws according to which the one appearance will be succeeded by the other, but there is no reason except prejudice for regarding both as appearances of the same substance.

One task, if what has just been said is correct, which confronts us in trying to connect the world of sense with the world of physics, is the task of reconstructing the conception of matter without the *a priori* beliefs which historically gave rise to it. In spite of the revolutionary results of modern physics, the empirical successes of the conception of matter show that there must be some legitimate conception which fulfils roughly the same functions. The time has hardly come when we can state precisely what this legitimate conception is, but we can see in a general way what it must be like. For this purpose, it is only necessary to take our ordinary common-sense statements and reword them without the assumption of permanent substance. We say, for example, that things change gradually—sometimes very quickly, but not without passing through a continuous or nearly continuous series of intermediate states. What this means is that, given any sensible appearance, there will usually be, *if we watch,* a continuous series of appearances connected with the given one, leading on by imperceptible gradations to the new appearances which common sense regards as those of the same thing. Thus a thing may be defined as a certain series of appearances, connected with each other by continuity and by certain causal laws. In the case of slowly changing things, this is easily seen. Consider, say, a wall-paper which fades in the course of years. It is an effort not to conceive of it as one "thing" whose colour is slightly different at one time from what it is at another. But what do we really *know* about it? We know that under suitable circumstances—i.e. when we are, as is said, "in the room"—we perceive certain colours in a certain pattern: not always precisely the same colours, but sufficiently similar to feel familiar. If we can state the laws according to which the colour varies, we can state all that is empirically verifiable; the assumption that there is a constant entity, the wall-paper, which "has" these various colours at various times, is a piece of gratuitous metaphysics. We may, if we like, *define* the wall-paper as the series of its aspects. These are collected together by the same motives which led us to regard the wall-paper as one thing, namely a combination of sensible continuity and causal connection. More generally, a "thing" will be defined as a certain series of aspects, namely those which would commonly be said to be *of* the thing. To say that a certain aspect is an aspect *of* a certain thing will merely mean that it is one of those which, taken serially, *are* the thing. Everything will then proceed as before: whatever was verifiable is unchanged, but our language is so interpreted as to avoid an unnecessary metaphysical assumption of permanence.

The above extrusion of permanent things affords an example of the maxim which inspires all scientific philosophising, namely "Occam's razor": *Entities are not to be multiplied without necessity*. In other words, in dealing with any subject-matter, find out what entities are undeniably involved, and state everything in terms of these entities. Very often the resulting statement is more complicated and difficult than one which, like common sense and most philosophy, assumes hypothetical entities whose existence there is no good reason to believe in. We find it easier to imagine a wall-paper with changing colours than to think merely of the series of colours; but it is a mistake to suppose that what is easy and natural in thought is what is more free from unwarrantable assumptions, as the case of "things" very aptly illustrates.

The above summary account of the genesis of "things," though it may be correct in outline, has omitted some serious difficulties which it is necessary briefly to consider. Starting from a world of helter-skelter sense-data, we wish to collect them into series, each of which can be regarded as consisting of the successive appearances of one "thing." There is, to begin with, some conflict between what common sense regards as one thing, and what physics regards as an unchanging collection of particles. To common sense, a human body is one thing, but to science the matter composing it is continually changing. This conflict, however, is not very serious, and may, for our rough preliminary purpose, be largely ignored. The problem is: by what principles shall we select certain data from the chaos, and call them all appearances of the same thing?

A rough and approximate answer to this question is not very difficult. There are certain fairly stable collections of appearances, such as landscapes, the furniture of rooms, the faces of acquaintances. In these cases, we have little hesitation in regarding them on successive occasions as appearances of one thing or collection of things. But, as the *Comedy of Errors* illustrates, we may be led astray if we judge by mere resemblance. This shows that something more is involved, for two different things may have any degree of likeness up to exact similarity.

Another insufficient criterion of one thing is *continuity*. As we have already seen, if we watch what we regard as one changing thing, we usually find its changes to be continuous so far as our senses can perceive. We are thus led to assume that, if we see two finitely different appearances at two different times, and if we have reason to regard them as belonging to the same thing, then there was a continuous series of intermediate states of that thing during the time when we were not observing it. And so it comes to be thought that continuity of change is necessary and sufficient to constitute one thing. But in fact it is neither. It is not *necessary*, because the unobserved states, in the case where our attention has not been concentrated on the thing throughout, are purely hypothetical, and cannot possibly be our ground for supposing the earlier and later appearances to belong to the same thing; on the contrary, it is because we suppose this that we assume intermediate unobserved states. Continuity is also not sufficient, since we can, for example, pass by sensibly continuous gradations from any one drop of the sea to any other drop. The utmost we can say is that discontinuity during uninterrupted observation is as a rule a mark of difference between things, though even this cannot be said in such cases as sudden explosions.

The assumption of continuity is, however, successfully made in physics (apart, perhaps, from quantum phenomena). This proves something, though not anything of very obvious utility to our present problem: it proves that nothing in the known world is inconsistent with the hypothesis that all changes are really continuous, though from too great rapidity or from our lack of observation they may not always appear continuous. In this hypothetical sense, continuity may be allowed to be a *necessary* condition if two appearances are to be classed as appearances of the same thing. But it is not a *sufficient* condition, as appears from the instance of the drops in the sea. Thus something more must be sought before we can give even the roughest definition of a "thing."

What is wanted further seems to be something in the nature of fulfilment of causal laws. This statement, as it stands, is very vague, but we will endeavour to give it precision. When I speak of "causal laws," I mean any laws which connect events at different times, or even, as a limiting case, events at the same time provided the connection is not logically demonstrable. In this very general sense, the laws of dynamics are causal laws, and so are the laws correlating the simultaneous appearances of one "thing" to different senses. The question is: How do such laws help in the definition of a "thing"?

To answer this question, we must consider what it is that is proved by the empirical success of physics. What is proved is that its hypotheses, though unverifiable where they go beyond sense-data, are at no point in contradiction with sense-data, but, on the contrary, are ideally such as to render all sense-data calculable from a sufficient collection of data all belonging to a given period of time. Now physics has found it empirically possible (apart from certain problems in quantum theory, as to which there is still uncertainty) to collect sense-data into series, each series being regarded as belonging to one "thing," and behaving, with regard to the laws of physics, in a way in which series not belonging to one thing would in general not behave. If it is to be unambiguous whether two appearances belong to the same thing or not, there must be only one way of grouping appearances so that the resulting things obey the laws of physics.

It would be very difficult to prove that this is the case, but for our present purposes we may let this point pass, and assume that there is only one way. We must include in our definition of a "thing" those of its aspects, if any, which are not observed. Thus we may lay down the following definition: *Things are those series of aspects which obey the laws of physics.* That such series exist is an empirical fact, which constitutes the verifiability of physics.

It may still be objected that the "matter" of physics is something other than series of sense-data. Sense-data, it may be said, belong to psychology and are, at any rate in some sense, subjective, whereas physics is quite independent of psychological considerations, and does not assume that its matter only exists when it is perceived.

To this objection there are two answers, both of some importance.

(a) We have been considering, in the above account, the question of the *verifiability* of physics. Now verifiability is by no means the same thing as truth; it is, in fact, something far more subjective and psychological. For a proposition to be verifiable, it is not enough that it should be true, but it must also be such as we can *discover* to be true. Thus verifiability depends upon our capacity for acquiring knowledge, and not only upon the objective truth. In physics, as ordinarily set forth, there is much that is unverifiable: there are hypotheses as to (α) how things would appear to a spectator in a place where, as it happens, there is no spectator; (β) how things would appear at times when, in fact, they are not appearing to anyone; (γ) things which never appear at all. All these are introduced to simplify the statement of the causal laws, but none of them forms an integral part of what is *known* to be true in physics. This brings us to our second answer.

(b) If physics is to consist wholly of propositions known to be true, or at least capable of being proved or disproved, the three kinds of hypothetical entities we have just enumerated must all be capable of being exhibited as logical functions of sense-data. In order to show how this might possibly be done, let us recall the hypothetical Leibnizian universe of Lecture III.[1]

Let us imagine that each mind looks out upon the world, as in Leibniz's monadology, from a point of view peculiar to itself; and for the sake of simplicity let us confine ourselves to the sense of sight, ignoring minds which are devoid of this sense. Each mind sees at each moment an immensely complex three-dimensional world; but there is absolutely nothing which is seen by two minds simultaneously. When we say that two people see the same thing, we always find that, owing to difference of point of view, there are differences, however slight, between their immediate sensible objects. (I am here assuming the validity of testimony, but as we are only constructing a *possible* theory, that is a legitimate assumption.) The three-dimensional world seen by one mind therefore contains no place in common with that seen by another, for places can only be constituted by the things in or around them. Hence we may suppose, in spite of the differences between the different worlds, that each exists entire exactly as it is perceived, and might be exactly as it is even if it were not perceived. We may further suppose that there are an infinite number of such worlds which are in fact unperceived. If two men are sitting in a room, two somewhat similar worlds are perceived by them; if a third man enters and sits between them, a third world, intermediate between the two previous worlds, begins to be perceived. It is true that we cannot reasonably suppose just this world to have existed before, because it is conditioned by the sense-organs, nerves, and brain of the newly arrived man; but we can reasonably suppose that *some* aspect of the universe existed from that point of view, though no one was perceiving it. The system consisting of all views of the universe perceived and unperceived, I shall call the system of "perspectives"; I shall confine the expression "private worlds" to

---

1 [The following is an insertion from pp. 92-98 from Lecture III of *Our Knowledge of the External World*, 2nd edn. Reprinted by permission of the publisher, George Allen & Unwin Ltd., London.]

such views of the universe as are actually perceived. Thus a "private world" is a perceived "perspective"; but there may be any number of unperceived perspectives.

Two men are sometimes found to perceive very similar perspectives, so similar that they can use the same words to describe them. They say they see the same table, because the differences between the two tables they see are slight and not practically important. Thus it is possible, sometimes, to establish a correlation by similarity between a great many of the things of one perspective, and a great many of the things of another. In case the similarity is very great, we say the points of view of the two perspectives are near together in space; but this space in which they are near together is totally different from the spaces inside the two perspectives. It is a relation between the perspectives, and is not in either of them; no one can perceive it, and if it is to be known it can be only by inference. Between two perceived perspectives which are similar, we can imagine a whole series of other perspectives, some at least unperceived, and such that between any two, however similar, there are others still more similar. In this way the space which consists in relations between perspectives can be rendered continuous, and (if we choose) three-dimensional.

We can now define the momentary common-sense "thing," as opposed to its momentary appearances. By the similarity of neighbouring perspectives, many objects in the one can be correlated with objects in the other, namely, with the similar objects. Given an object in one perspective, form the system of all the objects correlated with it in all the perspectives; that system may be identified with the momentary common-sense "thing." Thus an aspect of a "thing" is a member of the system of aspects which *is* the "thing" at that moment. (The correlation of the times of different perspectives raises certain complications, of the kind considered in the theory of relativity; but we may ignore these at present.) All the aspects of a thing are real, whereas the thing is a mere logical construction. It has, however, the merit of being neutral as between different points of view, and of being visible to more than one person, in the only sense in which it can ever be visible, namely, in the sense that each person sees one of its aspects.

It will be observed that, while each perspective contains its own space, there is only one space in which the perspectives themselves are the elements. There are as many private spaces as there are perspectives; there are therefore at least as many as there are percipients, and there may be any number of others which have a merely material existence and are not seen by anyone. But there is only one perspective-space, whose elements are single perspectives, each with its own private space. We have now to explain how the private space of a single perspective is correlated with part of the one all-embracing perspective space.

Perspective space is the system of "points of view" of private spaces (perspectives), or, since "points of view" have not been defined, we may say it is the system of the private spaces themselves. These private spaces will each count as one point, or at any rate as one element, in perspective space. They are ordered by means of their similarities. Suppose, for example, that we start from one which contains the appearance of a circular disc, such as would be called a penny, and suppose this appearance, in the perspective in question, is circular, not elliptic. We can then form a whole series of perspectives containing a graduated series of circular aspects of varying sizes: for this purpose we only have to move (as we say) towards the penny or away from it. The perspectives in which the penny looks circular will be said to lie on a straight line in perspective space, and their order on this line will be that of the sizes of the circular aspects. More-over—though this statement must be noticed and subsequently examined—the perspectives in which the penny looks big will be said to be nearer to the penny than those in which it looks small. It is to be remarked also that any other "thing" than our penny might have been chosen to define the relations of our perspectives in perspective space, and that experience shows that the same spatial order of perspectives would have resulted.

In order to explain the correlation of private spaces with per-spective space, we have first to explain what is meant by "the place (in perspective space) where a thing is." For this purpose, let us again consider the penny which appears in many perspectives. We formed a straight line of perspectives in which the penny looked circular, and we agreed that those in which it looked larger were to be considered as nearer to the penny. We can form another straight line of perspectives in which the penny is seen end-on and looks like a straight line of a certain thickness. These two lines will meet in a certain place in perspective space, i.e. in a certain perspective, which may be defined as "the place (in perspective space) where the penny is." It is true that, in order to prolong our lines until they reach this place, we shall have to make use of other things besides the penny, because, so far as experience goes, the penny ceases to present any appearance after we have come so near to it that it touches the eye. But this raises no real difficulty, because the spatial order of perspectives is found empirically to be independent of the particular "things" chosen for defining the order. We can, for example, remove our penny and prolong each of our two straight lines up to their intersection by placing other pennies further off in such a way that the aspects of the one are circular where those of our original penny were circular, and the aspects of the other are straight where those of our original penny were straight. There will then be just one perspective in which one of the new pennies looks circular and the other straight. This will be, by definition, the place where the original penny was in perspective space.

The above is, of course, only a first rough sketch of the way in which our definition is to be reached. It neglects the size of the penny, and it assumes that we can remove the penny without being disturbed by any simultaneous changes in the positions of other things. But it is plain that such niceties cannot affect the principle, and can only introduce complications in its application.

Having now defined the perspective which is the place where a given thing is, we can understand what is meant by saying that the perspectives in which a thing looks large are nearer to the thing than those in which it looks small: they are, in fact, nearer to the perspective which is the place where the thing is.

We can now also explain the correlation between a private space and parts of perspective space. If there is an aspect of a given thing in a certain private space, then we correlate the place where this aspect is in the private space with the place where the thing is in perspective space.

We may define "here" as the place, in perspective space, which is occupied by our private world. Thus we can now understand what is meant by speaking of a thing as near to or far from "here." A thing is near to "here" if the place where it is is near to my private world. We can also understand what is meant by saying that our private world is inside our head; for our private world is a place in perspective space, and may be part of the place where our head is.

It will be observed that *two* places in perspective space are associated with every aspect of a thing: namely, the place where the thing is, and the place which is the perspective of which the aspect in question forms part. Every aspect of a thing is a member of two different classes of aspects, namely: (1) the various aspects of the thing, of which at most one appears in any given perspective; (2) the perspective of which the given aspect is a member, i.e., that in which the thing has the given aspect. The physicist naturally classifies aspects in the first way, the psychologist in the second. The two places associated with a single aspect correspond to the two ways of classifying it. We may distinguish the two places as that *at* which, and that *from* which, the aspect appears. The "place at which" is the place of the thing to which the aspect belongs; the "place from which" is the place of the perspective to which the aspect belongs.

Let us now endeavour to state the fact that the aspect which a thing presents at a given place is affected by the intervening medium. The aspects of a thing in different perspectives are to be conceived as spreading outwards from the place where the thing is, and undergoing various changes as they get further away from this place. The laws according to which they change cannot be stated if we only take account of the aspects that are near the thing, but require that we should also take account of

the things that are at the places from which these aspects appear. This empirical fact can, therefore, be interpreted in terms
of our construction.[1]

In that universe we had a number of perspectives, two of which
never had any entity in common, but often contained entities
which could be sufficiently correlated to be regarded as belonging to the same thing. We will call one of these an "actual"
private world when there is an actual spectator to which it appears, and "ideal" when it is merely constructed on principles
of continuity. A physical thing consists, at each instant, of the
whole set of its aspects at that instant, in all the different worlds;
thus a momentary state of a thing is a whole set of aspects. An
"ideal" appearance will be an aspect merely calculated, but not
actually perceived by any spectator. An "ideal" state of a thing
will be a state at a moment when all its appearances are
ideal. An ideal thing will be one whose states at all times are
ideal. Ideal appearances, states, and things, since they are calculated, must be functions of actual appearances, states, and
things; in fact, ultimately, they must be functions of actual appearances. Thus it is unnecessary, for the enunciation of the
laws of physics, to assign any reality to ideal elements: it is
enough to accept them as logical constructions, provided we
have means of knowing how to determine when they become
actual. This, in fact, we have with some degree of approximation; the starry heaven, for instance, becomes actual whenever
we choose to look at it. It is open to us to believe that the ideal
elements exist, and there can be no reason for *dis*believing this;
but unless in virtue of some *a priori* law we cannot *know* it,
for empirical knowledge is confined to what we actually observe.

Permanent things, even as a logical construction, are no
longer quite adequate to the needs of physics. It seems that the
persistence of electrons and protons is only an approximate fact.
After a quantum change in an atom, according to Heisenberg,
we can no longer identify a given electron with a definite one

1 [End of Lecture III insert. Lecture IV resumes.]

of those existing before the change. Moreover, it is thought that, in the stars, an electron and a proton sometimes destroy each other, with the result that their energy (or mass) is converted into a non-material form. In fact, the difference between matter and other forms of energy has become much less than it used to be before energy and mass were found to be the same thing.

(2) The three main conceptions of physics are space, time, and matter. Some of the problems raised by the conception of matter have been indicated in the above discussion of "things." But space and time also raise difficult problems of much the same kind, namely, difficulties in reducing the haphazard untidy world of immediate sensation to the smooth orderly world of geometry and kinematics. Let us begin with the consideration of space.

People who have never read any psychology seldom realise how much mental labour has gone into the construction of the one all-embracing space into which all one man's sensible objects are supposed to fit. Kant, who was unusually ignorant of psychology, described space as "an infinite given whole," whereas a moment's psychological reflection shows that a space which is infinite is not given, while a space which can be called given is not infinite. What the nature of "given" space really is, is a difficult question, upon which psychologists are by no means agreed. But some general remarks may be made, which will suffice to show the problems, without taking sides on any psychological issue still in debate.

The first thing to notice is that different senses have different spaces. The space of sight is quite different from the space of touch: it is only by experience in infancy that we learn to correlate them. In later life, when we see an object within reach, we know how to touch it, and more or less what it will feel like; if we touch an object with our eyes shut, we know where we should have to look for it, and more or less what it would look like. But this knowledge is derived from early experience of the correlation of certain kinds of touch-sensations with certain kinds of sight-sensations. The one space into which both kinds of sensations fit is a construction, not a datum. And besides touch and sight, there are other kinds of sensation which give other, though less important, spaces: these also have to be fitted into the one space by means of experienced correlations. And as in the case of things, so here: the one all-embracing space, though convenient as a way of speaking, need not be supposed really to exist. All that experience makes certain is the several spaces of the several senses, correlated by empirically discovered laws. The one space may turn out to be valid as a logical construction, compounded of the several spaces, but there is no good reason to assume its independent metaphysical reality.

Another respect in which the spaces of immediate experience differ from the space of geometry and physics is in regard to *points*. The space of geometry and physics consists of an infinite number of points, but no one has ever seen or touched a point. If there are points in a sensible space, they must be an inference. It is not easy to see any way in which, as independent entities, they could be validly inferred from the data; thus here again, we shall have, if possible, to find some logical construction, some complex assemblage of immediately given objects, which will have the geometrical properties required of points. It is customary to think of points as simple and infinitely small, but geometry in no way demands that we should think of them in this way. All that is necessary for geometry is that they should have mutual relations possessing certain enumerated abstract properties, and it may be that an assemblage of data of sensation will serve this purpose. Exactly how this is to be done, I do not yet know, but it seems fairly certain that it can be done.

The following illustrative method, simplified so as to be easily manipulated, has been invented by Dr. Whitehead for the purpose of showing how points might be manufactured from sense-data.[1] We have first of all to observe that there are no infinitesimal sense-data: any surface we can see, for example, must be of some finite extent. But what at first appears as one undivided whole is often found, under the influence of attention, to split up into parts contained within the whole. Thus

---

[1] For his later method, see his *Concept of Nature*. See also my *Analysis of Matter,* Chapter XXVIII.

one spatial object may be contained within another, and entirely enclosed by the other. This relation of enclosure, by the help of some very natural hypotheses, will enable us to define a "point" as a certain class of spatial objects, namely all those (as it will turn out in the end) which would naturally be said to contain the point. In order to obtain a definition of a "point" in this way, we proceed as follows:

Given any set of volumes, or surfaces, they will not in general converge into one point. But if they get smaller and smaller, while of any two of the set there is always one that encloses the other, then we begin to have the kind of conditions which would enable us to treat them as having a point for their limit. The hypotheses required for the relation of enclosure are that (1) it must be transitive; (2) of two *different* spatial objects, it is impossible for each to enclose the other, but a single spatial object always encloses itself; (3) any set of spatial objects such that there is at least one spatial object enclosed by them all has a lower limit or minimum, i.e. an object enclosed by all of them and enclosing all objects which are enclosed by all of them; (4) to prevent trivial exceptions, we must add that there are to be instances of enclosure, i.e. there are really to be objects of which one encloses the other. When an enclosure-relation has these properties, we will call it a "point-producer." Given any relation of enclosure, we will call a set of objects an "enclosure-series" if, of any two of them, one is contained in the other. We require a condition which shall secure that an enclosure-series converges to a point, and this is obtained as follows: Let our enclosure-series be such that, given any other enclosure-series of which there are members enclosed in any arbitrarily chosen member of our first series, then there are members of our first series enclosed in any arbitrarily chosen member of our second series. In this case, our first enclosure-series may be called a "punctual enclosure-series." Then a "point" is all the objects which enclose members of a given punctual enclosure-series. In order to ensure infinite divisibility, we require one further property to be added to those defining point-producers, namely that any object which encloses itself also encloses an object other than itself. The "points" generated by point-producers with this property will be found to be such as geometry requires.[1]

The question of time, so long as we confine ourselves to one private world, is rather less complicated than that of space, and we can see pretty clearly how it might be dealt with by such methods as we have been considering. Events of which we are conscious do not last merely for a mathematical instant, but always for some finite time, however short. Even if there be a physical world such as the mathematical theory of motion supposes, impressions on our sense-organs produce sensations which are not merely and strictly instantaneous, and therefore the objects of sense of which we are immediately conscious are not strictly instantaneous. Instants, therefore, are not among the data of experience, and, if legitimate, must be either inferred or constructed. It is difficult to see how they can be validly inferred; thus we are left with the alternative that they must be constructed. How is this to be done?

Immediate experience provides us with two time-relations among events: they may be simultaneous, or one may be earlier and the other later. These two are both part of the crude data; it is not the case that only the events are given, and their time-order is added by our subjective activity. The time-order, within certain limits, is as much given as the events. In any story of adventure you will find such passages as the following: "With a cynical smile he pointed the revolver at the breast of the dauntless youth. 'At the word *three* I shall fire,' he said. The words one and two had already been spoken with a cool and deliberate distinctness. The word *three* was forming on his lips. At this moment a blinding flash of lightning rent the air." Here we have simultaneity—not due, as Kant would have us believe, to the subjective mental apparatus of the dauntless youth, but given as objectively as the revolver and the lightning. And it is equally given in immediate experience that the words *one* and *two* come earlier than the flash. These time-relations hold be-

[1] The above method requires certain improvements, which will be found in Whitehead, *loc. cit.*

tween events which are not strictly instantaneous. Thus one event may begin sooner than another, and therefore be before it, but may continue after the other has begun, and therefore be also simultaneous with it. If it persists after the other is over, it will also be later than the other. Earlier, simultaneous, and later, are not inconsistent with each other when we are concerned with events which last for a finite time, however short; they only become inconsistent when we are dealing with something instantaneous.

It is to be observed that we cannot give what may be called *absolute* dates, but only dates determined by events. We cannot point to a time itself, but only to some event occurring at that time. There is therefore no reason in experience to suppose that there are times as opposed to events: the events, ordered by the relations of simultaneity and succession, are all that experience provides. Hence, unless we are to introduce superfluous metaphysical entities, we must, in defining what mathematical physics can regard as an instant, proceed by means of some construction which assumes nothing beyond events and their temporal relations.

If we wish to assign a date exactly by means of events, how shall we proceed? If we take any one event, we cannot assign our date exactly, because the event is not instantaneous, that is to say, it may be simultaneous with two events which are not simultaneous with each other. In order to assign a date exactly, we must be able, theoretically, to determine whether any given event is before, at, or after this date, and we must know that any other date is either before or after this date, but not simultaneous with it. Suppose, now, instead of taking one event A, we take two events A and B, and suppose A and B partly overlap, but B ends before A ends. Then an event which is simultaneous with both A and B must exist during the time when A and B overlap; thus we have come rather nearer to a precise date than when we considered A and B alone. Let C be an event which is simultaneous with both A and B, but which ends before either A or B has ended. Then an event which is simultaneous with A and B and C must exist during the time when all three

A

B

C

overlap, which is a still shorter time. Proceeding in this way, by taking more and more events, a new event which is dated as simultaneous with all of them becomes gradually more and more accurately dated. This suggests a way by which a completely accurate date can be defined.

Let us take a group of events of which any two overlap, so that there is some time, however short, when they all exist. If there is any other event which is simultaneous with all of these, let us add it to the group; let us go on until we have constructed a group such that no event outside the group is simultaneous with all of them, but all the events inside the group are simultaneous with each other. Let us define this whole group as an instant of time. It remains to show that it has the properties we expect of an instant.

What are the properties we expect of instants? First, they must form a series: of any two, one must be before the other, and the other must be not before the one; if one is before another, and the other before a third, the first must be before the third. Secondly, every event must be at a certain number of instants; two events are simultaneous if they are at the same instant, and one is before the other if there is an instant, at which the one is, which is earlier than some instant at which the other is. Thirdly, if we assume that there is always some change going on somewhere during the time when any given event persists, the series of instants ought to be compact, i.e. given any two instants, there ought to be other instants between them. Do instants, as we have defined them, have these properties?

We shall say that an event is "at" an instant when it is a member of the group by which the instant is constituted; and we shall say that one instant is before another if the group which is the one instant contains an event which is earlier than, but not simultaneous with, some event in the group which is the other instant. When one event is earlier than, but not simultaneous with another, we shall say that it "wholly precedes" the other. Now we know that of two events which are not simultaneous, there must be one which wholly precedes the other, and in that case the other cannot also wholly precede the one; we also know that, if one event wholly precedes another, and the other wholly precedes a third, then the first wholly precedes the third. From these facts it is easy to deduce that the instants as we have defined them form a series.

We have next to show that every event is "at" at least one instant, i.e. that, given any event, there is at least one class, such as we used in defining instants, of which it is a member. For this purpose, consider all the events which are simultaneous with a given event, and do not begin later, i.e. are not wholly after anything simultaneous with it. We will call these the "initial contemporaries" of the given event. It will be found that this class of events is the first instant at which the given event exists, provided every event wholly after some contemporary of the given event is wholly after some *initial* contemporary of it.

Finally, the series of instants will be compact if, given any two events of which one wholly precedes the other, there are events wholly after the one and simultaneous with something wholly before the other. Whether this is the case or not, is an empirical question; but if it is not, there is no reason to expect the time-series to be compact.[1]

[1] The assumptions made concerning time-relations in the above are as follows:—
  I. In order to secure that instants form a series, we assume:
    (a) No event wholly precedes itself. (An "event" is defined as whatever is simultaneous with something or other.)
    (b) If one event wholly precedes another, and the other wholly precedes a third, then the first wholly precedes the third.
    (c) If one event wholly precedes another, it is not simultaneous with it.

Thus our definition of instants secures all that mathematics requires, without having to assume the existence of any disputable metaphysical entities.

Instants may also be defined by means of the enclosure-relation, exactly as was done in the case of points. One object will be temporally enclosed by another when it is simultaneous with the other, but not before or after it. Whatever encloses temporally or is enclosed temporally we shall call an "event." In order that the relation of temporal enclosure may be a "point-producer," we require (1) that it should be transitive, i.e. that if one event encloses another, and the other a third, then the first encloses the third; (2) that every event encloses itself, but if one event encloses another different event, then the other does not enclose the one; (3) that given any set of events such that there is at least one event enclosed by all of them, then there is an event enclosing all that they all enclose, and itself enclosed by all of them; (4) that there is at least one event. To ensure infinite divisibility, we require also that every event should enclose events other than itself. Assuming these characteristics, temporal enclosure is an infinitely divisible point-producer. We can now form an "enclosure-series" of events, by choosing a

---

      (d) Of two events which are not simultaneous, one must wholly precede the other.
  II. In order to secure that the initial contemporaries of a given event should form an instant, we assume:
      (e) An event wholly after some contemporary of a given event is wholly after some *initial* contemporary of the given event.
 III. In order to secure that the series of instants shall be compact, we assume:
      (f) If one event wholly precedes another, there is an event wholly after the one and simultaneous with something wholly before the other.
This assumption entails the consequence that if one event covers the whole of a stretch of time immediately preceding another event, then it must have at least one instant in common with the other event; i.e., it is impossible for one event to cease just before another begins. I do not know whether this should be regarded as inadmissible. For a mathematicological treatment of the above topics, *cf.* N. Wiener, "A Contribution to the Theory of Relative Position," *Proc. Camb. Phil. Soc.*, xvii, 5, pp. 441-449.

group of events such that of any two there is one which encloses the other; this will be a "punctual enclosure-series" if, given any other enclosure-series such that every member of our first series encloses some member of our second, then every member of our second series encloses some member of our first. Then an "instant" is the class of all events which enclose members of a given punctual enclosure-series.[1]

The correlation of the times of different private worlds so as to produce the one all-embracing time of traditional physics is only approximately possible, for the reasons which led to the theory of relativity. So long as we confine ourselves to the surfaces of the earth, the approximation is very nearly exact. We saw, in Lecture III, that different private worlds often contain correlated appearances, such as common sense would regard as appearances of the same "thing." When two appearances in different worlds are so correlated as to belong to one momentary "state" of a thing, it would be natural to regard them as simultaneous, and as thus affording a simple means of correlating different private times. But this can only be regarded as a first approximation. What we call one sound will be heard sooner by people near the source of the sound than by people farther from it, and the same applies, though in a less degree, to light. Thus two correlated appearances in different worlds are not necessarily to be regarded as occurring at the same date in physical time, though they will be parts of one momentary state of a thing. The correlation of different private times is regulated by the desire to secure the simplest possible statement of the laws of physics, and thus raises rather complicated technical problems; but from the point of view

---

[1] [For Russell's method of constructing points and instants in his later philosophy of science, see below, Part III, Chapter III. See also Russell's *The Analysis of Matter,* Chapters XXVIII and XXIX. Further discussions can be found in A. N. Whitehead, *An Enquiry Concerning the Principles of Natural Knowledge* (1919), Part III, and *The Concept of Nature* (1920), Chapters III and IV. An exposition of Russell's various methods can be found in C. A. Fritz, Jr., *Bertrand Russell's Construction of the External World* (London: Routledge and Kegan Paul, 1952), pp. 180 ff., and C. D. Broad, *Scientific Thought* (1923), Chapter I.]

of philosophical theory, there is no very serious difficulty of principle involved, within the limits imposed by the theory of relativity.

The above brief outline must not be regarded as more then tentative and suggestive. It is intended merely to show the kind of way in which, given a world with the kind of properties that psychologists find in the world of sense, it may be possible, by means of purely logical constructions, to make it amenable to mathematical treatment by defining series or classes of sense-data which can be called respectively particles, points, and instants. If such constructions are possible, then mathematical physics is applicable to the real world, in spite of the fact that its particles, points, and instants are not to be found among actually existing entities.

The space-time of physics has not a very close relation to the space and time of the world of one person's experience. Everything that occurs in one person's experience must, from the standpoint of physics, be located within that person's body; this is evident from considerations of causal continuity. What occurs when I see a star occurs as the result of light-waves impinging on the retina, and causing a process in the optic nerve and brain; therefore the occurrence called "seeing a star" must be in the brain. If we define a piece of matter as a set of events (as was suggested above), the sensation of seeing a star will be one of the events which *are* the brain of the percipient at the time of the perception. Thus every event that I experience will be one of the events that constitute some part of my body. The space of (say) my visual perceptions is only *correlated* with physical space, more or less approximately: from the physical point of view, whatever I see is inside my head. I do not see physical objects; I see effects which they produce in the region where my brain is. The correlation of visual and physical space is rendered approximate by the fact that my visual sensations are not *wholly* due each to some physical object, but also partly to the intervening medium. Further, the relation of visual sensation to physical object is one-many, not one-one, because our senses are more or less vague: things which look different under the microscope may be indistinguishable to the naked eye. The inferences from perceptions to physical facts depend always upon causal laws, which enable us to bring past history to bear: e.g. if we have just examined an object under a microscope, we assume that it is still very similar to what we then saw it to be, or rather, to what we inferred it to be from what we then saw. It is through history and testimony, together with causal laws, that we arrive at physical knowledge which is much more precise that anything inferable from the perceptions of one moment. History, testimony, and causal laws are, of course, in their various degrees, open to question. But we are not now considering whether physics is true, but now, if it is true, its world is related to that of the senses.

With regard to time, the relation of psychology to physics is surprisingly simple. The time of our experience is the time which results, in physics, from taking our own body as the origin. Seeing that all the events in my experience are, for physics, in my body, the time-interval between them is what relativity theory calls the "interval" (in space-time) between them. Thus the time-interval between two events in one person's experience retains a direct physical significance in the theory of relativity. But the merging of physical space and time into space-time does not correspond to anything in psychology. Two events which are simultaneous in my experience may be spatially separate in physical space, e.g. when I see two stars at once. But in physical space these two events are not separated, and indeed they occur at the same place in space-time. Thus in this respect relativity theory has complicated the relation between perception and physics.

The problem which the above considerations are intended to elucidate is one whose importance and even existence has been concealed by the unfortunate separation of different studies which prevails throughout the civilised world. Physicists, ignorant and contemptuous of philosophy, have been content to assume their particles, points, and instants in practice, while conceding, with ironical politeness, that their concepts laid no claim to metaphysical validity. Metaphysicians, obsessed by the idealistic opinion that only mind is real, and the Parmenidean belief that the real is unchanging, repeated one after another the supposed contradictions in the notions of matter, space, and time, and therefore naturally made no endeavour to invent a tenable theory of particles, points, and instants. Psychologists, who have done invaluable work in bringing to light the chaotic nature of the crude materials supplied by unmanipulated sensation, have been ignorant of mathematics and modern logic, and have therefore been content to say that matter, space, and time are "intellectual constructions," without making any attempt to show in detail either how the intellect can construct them, or what secures the practical validity which physics shows them to possess. Philosophers, it is to be hoped, will come to recognise that they cannot achieve any solid success in such problems without some slight knowledge of logic, mathematics, and physics; meanwhile, for want of students with the necessary equipment, this vital problem remains unattempted and unknown.

There are, it is true, two authors, both physicists, who have done something, though not much, to bring about a recognition of the problem as one demanding study. These two authors are Poincaré and Mach, Poincaré especially in his *Science and Hypothesis,* Mach especially in his *Analysis of Senations.* Both of them, however, admirable as their work is, seem to me to suffer from a general philosophical bias. Poincaré is Kantian, while Mach is ultra-empiricist; with Poincaré almost all the mathematical part of physics is merely conventional, while with Mach the difficulties of a purely sensational physics are somewhat underestimated. Nevertheless, both these authors, and especially Mach, deserve mention as having made serious contributions to the consideration of our problem.[1]

When a point or an instant is defined as a class of sensible qualities, the first impression produced is likely to be one of wild and wilful paradox. Certain considerations apply here,

[1] Since 1914, when the above was written, much admirable work has been done on the above topics. I should mention especially, as of first-class importance, the work of Whitehead, Eddington, and Heisenberg.

however, which will again be relevant when we come to the definition of numbers. There is a whole type of problems which can be solved by such definitions, and almost always there will be at first an effect of paradox. Given a set of objects any two of which have a relation of the sort called "symmetrical and transitive," it is almost certain that we shall come to regard them as all having some common quality, or as all having the same relation to some one object outside the set. This kind of case is important, and I shall therefore try to make it clear even at the cost of some repetition of previous definitions.

A relation is said to be "symmetrical" when, if one term has this relation to another, then the other also has it to the one. Thus "brother or sister" is a "symmetrical" relation: if one person is a brother or a sister of another, then the other is a brother or sister of the one. Simultaneity, again, is a symmetrical relation; so is equality in size. A relation is said to be "transitive" when, if one term has this relation to another, and the other to a third, then the one has it to the third. The symmetrical relations mentioned just now are also transitive—provided, in the case of "brother or sister," we allow a person to be counted as his or her own brother or sister, and provided, in the case of simultaneity, we mean complete simultaneity, i.e. beginning and ending together.

But many relations are transitive without being symmetrical —for instance, such relations as "greater," "earlier," "to the right of," "ancestor of," in fact all such relations as give rise to series. Other relations are symmetrical without being transitive—for example, difference in any respect. If A is of a different age from B, and B of a different age from C, it does not follow that A is of a different age from C. Simultaneity, again, in the case of events which last for a finite time, will not necessarily be transitive if it only means that the times of the two events overlap. If A ends just after B has begun, and B ends just after C has begun, A and B will be simultaneous in this sense, and so will B and C, but A and C may well not be simultaneous.

All the relations which can naturally be represented as equality in any respect, or as possession of a common property, are transitive and symmetrical—this applies, for example, to such relations as being of the same height or weight or colour. Owing to the fact that possession of a common property gives rise to a transitive symmetrical relation, we come to imagine that wherever such a relation occurs it must be due to a common property. "Being equally numerous" is a transitive symmetrical relation of two collections; hence we imagine that both have a common property, called their number. "Existing at a given instant" (in the sense in which we defined an instant) is a transitive symmetrical relation; hence we come to think that there really is an instant which confers a common property on all the things existing at that instant. "Being states of a given thing" is a transitive symmetrical relation; hence we come to imagine that there really is a thing, other than the series of states, which accounts for the transitive symmetrical relation. In all such cases, the class of terms that have the given transitive symmetrical relation to a given term will fulfil all the formal requisites of a common property of all the members of the class. Since there certainly is the class, while any other common property may be illusory, it is prudent, in order to avoid needless assumptions, to substitute the class for the common property which would be ordinarily assumed.[1] This is the reason for the definitions we have adopted, and this is the source of the apparent paradoxes. No harm is done if there are such common properties as language assumes, since we do not deny them, but merely abstain from asserting them. But if there are not such common properties in any given case, then our method has secured us against error. In the absence of special knowledge, therefore, the method we have adopted is the only one which is safe, and which avoids the risk of introducing fictitious metaphysical entities.

1 [Cf. Russell's *Principles of Mathematics* (1903), Chapters XXI, XXVI.]

PART THREE

PART THREE

PART THREE

Physics and Perception

In the preceding part we have seen that Russell developed an interpretation of science which based it upon sense data alone, and for which it was unnecessary to presuppose the usual belief in the reality of the external world. He maintained that this view provided an adequate interpretation of science, even though it seemed foreign to common sense. Russell became more and more impatient with this remoteness from common sense, and in 1927, in *The Analysis of Matter*, formulated a view which he hoped would do justice to both science and common sense. He was still concerned with showing that percepts (or 'sense data' in his earlier terminology) are the basis of empirical knowledge, and with isolating and justifying the inferences from percepts to scientific knowledge. Although science should be related to our perceptual experience, at the same time our basic common-sense belief in an external world should not be disregarded.

Russell develops the picture of the world that science gives by means of what he now finds to be the ultimate constituents of the world. These are 'events,' of which percepts are a subclass. Common-sense objects and scientific entities, e.g., points, instants, and electrons, can be

77

'constructed' out of events in a manner similar to their construction out of sense data. The world can now be seen to be composed of various groups of events, connected to each other in various ways to form 'causal chains,' the bases for the different activities and processes we find in the natural world. A world so composed of events provides a satisfactory interpretation of the abstract terms of physics, and at the same time is consistent with common-sense knowledge as well.

I believe that Russell still accepts in its essential features the view presented here. (See *My Philosophical Development*, 1959, Chapter Two.) Part Three consists of several chapters in which his view is developed in some detail, taken from Russell's later discussion in *Human Knowledge* (1948). Not included here is Russell's discussion of the interpretation of the more technical terms of physics by means of events; the reader is referred to *The Analysis of Matter* for these topics.

CHAPTER ONE

Physics and Experience

The question to be discussed in this chapter is one which, in my opinion, has been far too little considered. It is this: Assuming physics to be broadly speaking true, can we know it to be true, and, if the answer is to be in the affirmative, does this involve knowledge of other truths besides those of physics? We might find that, if the world is such as physics says it is, no organism could know it to be such; or that, if an organism can know it to be such, it must know some things other than physics, more particularly certain principles of probable inference.

This question becomes acute through the problem of perception. There have, from the earliest times, been two types of theory as to perception, one empirical, the other idealist. According to the empirical theory, some continuous chain of causation leads from the object to the percipient, and what is called "perceiving" the object is the last link in this chain, or rather the last before the chain begins to lead out of the percipient's body instead of into it. According to the idealist theory, when a percipient happens to be in the neighborhood of an object a divine illumination causes the percipient's soul to have an experience which is like the object.

Each of these theories has its difficulties.

The idealist theory has its origin in Plato, but reaches its logical culmination in Leibniz, who held that the world consists of monads which never interact, but which all go through parallel developments, so that what happens to me at any instant has a similarity to what is happening to you at the same instant. When you think you move your arm, I think I see you moving it; thus we are both deceived, and no one before Leibniz was sufficiently acute to unmask the deception, which he regards as the best proof of God's goodness. This theory is fantastic, and has had few adherents, but in less logical forms portions of the idealistic theory of perception are to be found even among those who think themselves most remote from it.

Philosophy is an offshoot of theology, and most philosophers, like Malvolio, "think nobly of the soul." They are therefore predisposed to endow it with magical powers, and to suppose that the relation between perceiving and what is perceived must be something utterly different from physical causation. This view is reinforced by the belief that mind and matter are completely disparate, and that perceiving, which is a mental phenomenon, must be totally unlike an occurrence in the brain, which is all that can be attributed to physical causation.

The theory that perceiving depends upon a chain of physical causation is apt to be supplemented by a belief that to every state of the brain a certain state of the mind "corresponds," and vice versa, so that given either the state of the brain or the state of the mind, the other could be inferred by a person who sufficiently understood the correspondence. If it is held that there is no causal interaction between mind and brain, this is merely a new form of the pre-established harmony. But if causation is regarded—as it usually is by empiricists—as nothing but invariable sequence or concomitance, then the supposed correspondence of brain and mind tautologically involves causal interaction. The whole question of the dependence of mind on body or body on mind has been involved in quite needless obscurity owing to the emotions involved. The facts are quite plain. Certain observable occurrences are commonly called "physical," certain others "mental"; sometimes "physical" occurrences appear as causes of "mental" ones, sometimes vice versa. A blow causes me to feel pain; a volition causes me to move my arm. There is no reason to question either of these causal connections, or at any rate no reason which does not apply to all causal connections equally.

These considerations remove one set of difficulties that stand in the way of acceptance of the physical theory of perception.

The common-sense arguments in favor of the physical causation of perceptions are so strong that only powerful prejudices could have caused them to be questioned. When we shut our eyes wo do not see; when we stop our ears we do not hear; when we are under an anesthetic we perceive nothing. The appearance that a thing presents can be altered by jaundice, short sight, microscopes, mists, etc. The time at which we hear a sound depends upon our distance from its physical point of origin. The same is true of what we see, though the velocity of light is so great that where terrestrial objects are concerned, the time between an occurrence and our seeing of it is inappreciable. If it is by a divine illumination that we perceive objects, it must be admitted that the illumination adapts itself to physical conditions.

There are, however, two objections to the physical causation of perceptions. One is that it makes it impossible, or at least very difficult, to suppose that external objects are what they seem to be; the other is that it seems to make it doubtful whether occurrences that we call "perceptions" can really be a source of knowledge as to the physical world. The first of these may be ignored as having only to do with prejudices, but the second is more important.

The problem is this: Every empiricist holds that our knowledge as to matters of fact is derived from perception, but if physics is true there must be so little resemblance between our percepts and their external causes that it is difficult to see how, from percepts, we can acquire a knowledge of external objects. The problem is further complicated by the fact that physics has been inferred from perception. Historically, physicists started from naïve realism, that is to say, from the belief that external objects are exactly as they seem. On the basis of this assumption, they developed a theory which made matter something quite unlike what we perceive. Thus their conclusion contradicted their premise, though no one except a few philosophers noticed this. We therefore have to decide whether, if physics is true, the hypothesis of naïve realism can be so modified that there shall be a valid inference from percepts to physics. In a word: If physics is true, is it possible that it should be known?

Let us first try to define what we are to mean by the hypothesis that physics is true. I want to adopt this hypothesis only to the extent to which it appeals to educated common sense. We find that the theories of physicists constantly undergo modification, so that no prudent man of science would expect any physical theory to be quite unchanged a hundred years hence. But when theories change, the alteration usually has only a small effect so far as observable phenomena are concerned. The *practical* difference between Einstein's theory of gravitation and Newton's is very minute, though the theoretical difference is very great. Moreover, in every new theory there are some parts that seem pretty certain, while others remain very speculative. Einstein's substitution of space-time for space and time represents a change of language for which there are the same sort of grounds of simplicity as there were for the Copernican change of language. This part of Einstein's theory may be accepted with considerable confidence. But the view that the universe is a three-dimensional sphere of finite diameter remains speculative; no one would be surprised if evidence were found which would lead astronomers to give up this way of speaking.

Or, again, take the physical theory of light. No one doubts that light travels at the rate of roughly 300,000 kilometers per second, but whether it consists of waves or of particles called photons is a matter as to which dispute has been possible. In the case of sound, on the other hand, the wave theory may be accepted as firmly established.

Every physical theory which survives goes through three stages. In the first stage, it is a matter of controversy among

specialists; in the second stage, the specialists are agreed that
it is the theory which best fits the available evidence, though
it may well hereafter be found incompatible with new evidence;
in the third stage, it is thought very unlikely that any new
evidence will do more than somewhat modify it.

When I say that I shall assume physics to be true, I mean that
I shall accept those parts of physics which have reached the
third stage, not as certain, but as more probable than any philosophical speculation, and therefore proper to be accepted by
philosophers as a premise in their arguments.

Let us now see what the most certain parts of physics have to
say that is relevant to our present problem.

The great physical discoveries of the seventeenth century
were made by means of two working hypotheses. One of these
was that causal laws in the physical world need only take account of matter and motion, matter being composed of particles
persisting through time but continuously changing their positions in space. It was assumed that, so far as physics is concerned, there is no need to take account of anything about a
particle except its position in space at various times; that is to
say, we might suppose particles to differ only in position, not in
quality. At first, this was hardly more than a definition of the
word "physics"; when it was necessary to take account of qualitative differences, we were concerned with a different subject,
called "chemistry." During the present century, however, the
modern theory of the atom has reduced chemistry, theoretically,
to physics. This has enormously extended the scope of the hypothesis that different particles of matter differ only in position.

Does this hypothesis apply also to physiology, or is the behavior of living matter subject to laws different from those
governing dead matter? Vitalists maintain the latter view, but
I think the former has the greater weight of authority in its
favor. What can be said is that wherever a physiological process
is understood, it is found to follow the laws of physics and chemistry, and that, further, there is no physiological process which
is clearly not explicable by these laws. It is therefore the best

hypothesis that physiology is reducible to physics and chemistry. But this hypothesis has not nearly the same degree of certainty as the reduction of chemistry to physics.

I shall assume henceforth that the first of the seventeenth-century working hypotheses, which may be called the hypothesis of the homogeneity of matter, applies throughout the physical world, and to living as well as dead matter: I shall not constantly repeat that this theory is not *certainly* true; this is to be taken as said once for all. I assume the theory because the weight of evidence, though not conclusive, seems to me strongly in its favor.

The second of the working hypotheses of the seventeenth century may be called the hypothesis of the independence of causes; it is embodied in the parallelogram law. In its simplest form it says such things as: If you walk for a minute on the deck of a moving ship, you will reach the same point, relatively to the water, as you would if first you stood still for a minute while the ship moved, and then the ship stood still for a minute while you did your walk on the deck. More generally, when a body is subject to several forces, the result of their all acting at once for a given length of time is the same as would be the result of their all acting by turns, each for the given length of time—or rather, if the given length of time is very short this will be nearly true, and the shorter the time the more nearly true it will become. For instance, the moon is attracted both by the earth and by the sun; in one second, it will move very nearly as if, for one second, it were not attracted by either, but went on moving as before, then for another second it were to move as if (starting from rest) it were attracted by the earth only, then for another second as if (starting from rest) it were attracted by the sun only. If we take a shorter time than a second this will be more nearly true, approaching the limit of complete truth as the period of time is indefinitely diminished.

This principle is of the utmost importance technically. It enables us, when we have studied the effects of a number of separate forces each acting singly, to calculate the effect of their all acting together. It is the basis of the mathematical methods employed in traditional physics. But it must be said that it is not self-evident, except in simple cases like that of the man walking on the deck of the ship. In other cases, it is to be believed if it works, but we ought not to be surprised if we find that it sometimes does not work. In the quantum theory of the atom it has had to be abandoned, though this is perhaps not definitive. However that may be, this second working hypothesis is much less securely established than the first. It holds, at least approximately, over a wide field, but there is no good ground for believing that it holds universally.

The present century has somewhat modified the assumptions of physics. First, there is a four-dimensional manifold of events, instead of the two manifolds of space and time; second, causal laws do not suffice to determine individual events, but only statistical distributions; third, change is probably discontinuous. These modifications would be more important to us than they are but for the fact that the second and third only apply effectively to microscopic phenomena, while the physical occurrences, such as speaking, which are associated with "mental" events, are macroscopic. Therefore, if a human body works wholly in accordance with physical laws, it will still be correct to use the laws of classical physics to determine what a man will say, and generally what will be the large-scale motions of his body.

This brings us to the problem of the relation of mind and matter, since perception is commonly considered "mental" while the object perceived and the stimulus to perceiving are considered "physical." My own belief is that there is no difficulty whatever about this problem. The supposed difficulties have their origin in bad metaphysics and bad ethics. Mind and matter, we are told, are two substances, and are utterly disparate. Mind is noble; matter is base. Sin consists in subjection of the mind to the body. Knowledge, being one of the noblest of mental activities, cannot depend upon sense, for sense marks a form of subjection to matter and is therefore bad. Hence the Platonic objection to identifying knowledge with perception.

All this, you may think, is antiquated, but it has left a trail of prejudices hard to overcome.

Nevertheless, the distinction of mind and matter would hardly have arisen if it had not some foundation. We must seek, therefore, for one or more distinctions more or less analogous to the distinction between mind and matter. I should define a "mental" occurrence as one which can be known without inference. But let us examine some more conventional definitions.

We cannot use the Cartesian distinction between thought and extension, if only on Leibniz's ground, that extension involves plurality and therefore cannot be an attribute of a single substance. But we might try a somewhat analogous distinction. Material things, we may say, have spatial relations, while mental things do not. The brain is in the head, but thoughts are not— so, at least, philosophers assure us. This point of view is due to a confusion between different meanings of the word "space." Among the things that I see at a given moment there are spatial relations which are a part of my percepts; if percepts are "mental," as I should contend, then spatial relations which are ingredients of percepts are also "mental." Naïve realism identifies my percepts with physical things; it assumes that the sun of the astronomers is what I see. This involves identifying the spatial relations of my percepts with those of physical things. Many people retain this aspect of naïve realism although they have rejected all the rest.

But this identification is indefensible. The spatial relations of physics hold between electrons, protons, neutrons, etc., which we do not perceive; the spatial relations of visual percepts hold between things that we do perceive, and in the last analysis between colored patches. There is a rough correlation between physical space and visual space, but it is very rough. First: depths become indistinguishable when they are great. Second: the timing is different; the place where the sun seems to be now corresponds to the place where the physical sun was eight minutes ago. Third: the percept is subject to changes which the physicist does not attribute to changes in the object; e.g., those brought about by clouds, telescopes, squinting, or closing the eyes. The correspondence between the percept and the physical object is therefore only approximate, and it is no more exact as regards spatial relations than it is in other respects. The sun of the physicist is not identical with the sun of my percepts, and the 93,000,000 miles that separate it from the moon are not identical with the spatial relation between the visual sun and the visual moon when I happen to see both at once.

When I say that something is "outside" me, there are two different things that I may mean. I may mean that I have a percept which is outside the percept of my body in perceptual space, or I may mean that there is a physical object which is outside my body as a physical object in the space of physics. Generally there is a rough correspondence between these two. The table that I see is outside my body as I see it in perceptual space, and the physical table is outside my physical body in physical space. But sometimes the correspondence fails. I dream, say, of a railway accident: I see the train falling down an embankment, and I hear the shrieks of the injured. These dream objects are genuinely and truly "outside" my dream body in my own perceptual space. But when I wake up I find that the whole dream was due to a noise in my ear. And when I say that the noise is in my ear, I mean that the physical source of the sound that I experience is "in" my ear as a physical object in physical space. In another sense, we might say that all noises are in the ear, but if we confuse these two senses the result is an inextricable tangle.

Generalizing, we may say that my percept of anything other than my body is "outside" the percept of my body in perceptual space, and if the perception is not misleading the physical object is "outside" my physical body in physical space. It does not follow that my percept is outside my physical body. Indeed, such a hypothesis is prima facie meaningless, although, as we shall see, a meaning can be found for it, and it is then false.

We can now begin to tackle our central question, namely, what do we mean by a "percept," and how can it be a source of knowledge as to something other than itself?

What is a "percept"? As I use the word, it is what happens
when, in common-sense terms, I see something or hear something
or otherwise believe myself to become aware of something
through my senses. The sun, we believe, is always there, but I
only sometimes see it: I do not see it at night, or in cloudy
weather, or when I am otherwise occupied. But sometimes I
see it. All the occasions on which I see the sun have a certain
resemblance to each other, which enabled me in infancy to
learn to use the word "sun" on the right occasions. Some of
the resemblances between different occasions when I see the sun
are obviously in me; for example: I must have my eyes open
and turn in the right direction. These, therefore, we do not
regard as properties of the sun. But there are other resemblances
which, so far as common sense can discover, do not depend upon us; when we see the sun, it is almost always round and bright
and hot. The few occasions when it is not are easily explicable
as due to fog or to an eclipse. Common sense therefore says:
There is an object which is round and bright and hot; the kind
of event called "seeing the sun" consists in a relation between
me and this object, and when this relation occurs I am "perceiving" the object.

But at this point physics intervenes in a very awkward way.
It assures us that the sun is not "bright" in the sense in which
we usually understand the word; it is a source of light rays
which have a certain effect upon eyes and nerves and brains, but
when this effect is absent because the light rays do not encounter
a living organism, there is nothing that can be properly called
"brightness." Exactly the same considerations apply to the
words "hot" and "round"—at least if "round" is understood
as a perceptible quality. Moreover, though you see the sun now,
the physical object to be inferred from your seeing existed eight
minutes ago; if, in the intervening minutes, the sun had gone
out, you would still be seeing exactly what you are seeing. We
cannot therefore identify the physical sun with what we see;
nevertheless what we see is our chief reason for believing in the
physical sun.

Assuming the truth of physics, what is there in its laws that justifies inferences from percepts to physical objects? Before we can adequately discuss this question, we must determine the place of percepts in the world of physics. There is here a peculiarity: physics never mentions percepts except when it speaks of empirical verification of its laws; but if its laws are not concerned with percepts, how can percepts verify them? This question should be borne in mind during the following discussions.

The question of the position of percepts in the causal chains of physics is a different one from that of the cognitive status of percepts, though the two are interconnected. At the moment I am concerned with the location of percepts in causal chains. Now, a percept—say hearing a noise—has a series of antecedents, which travel in space-time from the physical source of the noise through the air to the ears and brain. The experience which we call "hearing the noise" is as nearly as can be determined simultaneous with the cerebral term of the physical causal chain. If the noise is of the kind to call forth a bodily movement, the movement begins almost immediately after "hearing the noise." If we are going to fit "hearing the noise" into a physical causal chain, we must therefore connect it with the same region of space-time as that of the accompanying cerebral events. And this applies also to the noise as something perceived. The only region of space-time with which this noise has any direct connection is the present state of the hearer's brain; the connection with the physical source of the sound is indirect. Exactly the same argument applies to things seen.

I am anxious to minimize the metaphysical assumptions to be made in this connection. You may hold that mind and matter interact, or that, as the Cartesians contended, they run in parallel series, or that, as materialists believe, mental occurrences are mere concomitants of certain physical occurrences, determined by them but having no reciprocal influence on physical events. What you hold in these respects has no bearing on the point that I am making. What I am saying is something which is obvious to educated common sense, namely, that whether we consider the percept or the simultaneous state of the brain, the causal location of either is intermediate between occurrences in afferent nerves constituting the stimulus, and occurrences in efferent nerves constituting the reaction.

This applies not only to the perceiving, which we naturally regard as "mental," but to what we experience when we perceive. That is to say, it applies not only to "seeing the sun" but also to the sun, if we mean by "the sun" something that a human being can experience. The astronomer's sun is inferred, it is not hot or bright, and it existed eight minutes before what is called seeing it. If I see the sun and it makes me blink, what I see is not 93,000,000 miles and eight minutes away, but is causally (and therefore spatio-temporally) intermediate between the light waves striking the eye and the consequent blinking.

The dualistic view of perception, as a relation of a subject to an object, is one which, following the leadership of William James, empiricists have now for the most part abandoned. The distinction between "seeing the sun" as a mental event and the immediate object of my seeing is now generally rejected as invalid, and in this view I concur. But many of those who take the view that I take on this point nevertheless inconsistently adhere to some form of naïve realism. If my seeing of the sun is identical with the sun that I see, then the sun that I see is not the astronomer's sun. For exactly the same reasons, the tables and chairs that I see, if they are identical with my seeing of them, are not located where physics says they are but where my seeing is. You may say that my seeing, being mental, is not in space; if you do, I will not argue the point. But I shall none the less insist that there is one, and only one, region of space-time with which my seeing is always causally bound up, and that is my brain at the time of the seeing. And exactly the same is true of all objects of sense perception.

We are now in a position to consider the relation between a physical occurrence and the subsequent occurrence popularly regarded as seeing it. Consider, say, a flash of lightning on a dark night. The flash, for the physicist, is an electrical discharge, which causes electromagnetic waves to travel outward from the region where it has taken place. These waves, if they meet no opaque matter, merely travel farther and farther; but when they meet opaque matter their energy undergoes transformations into new forms. When they happen to meet a human eye connected with a human brain, all sorts of complicated things happen, which can be studied by the physiologist. At the moment when this causal process reaches the brain, the person to whom the brain belongs "sees" the flash. This person, if he is unacquainted with physics, thinks that the flash *is* what takes place when he "sees" the flash; or rather, he thinks that what takes place is a relation between himself and the flash, called "perceiving" the flash. If he is acquainted with physics, he does not think this, but he still holds that the sort of thing that takes place when he "sees" the flash gives an adequate basis for knowledge of the physical world.

We can now at last tackle the question: How, and to what extent, can percepts be a source of knowledge as to physical objects? A percept, we have agreed, comes at the end of a causal chain which starts at the object. (Of course no causal chain really has either a beginning or an end. From another point of view the percept is a beginning; it begins the reaction to a stimulus.) If the percept is to be a source of knowledge of the object, it must be possible to infer the cause from the effect, or at least to infer some characteristics of the cause. In this backward inference from effect to cause, I shall for the present assume the laws of physics.

If percepts are to allow inferences to objects, the physical world must contain more or less separable causal chains. I can see at the present moment various things—sheets of paper, books, trees, walls, and clouds. If the separateness of these things in my visual field is to correspond to a physical separateness, each of them must start its own causal chain, arriving at my eye without much interference from the others. The theory of light assures us that this is the case. Light waves emanating from a source will, in suitable circumstances, pursue their course practically unaffected by other light waves in the same region. But when light waves encounter a reflecting or refracting object this independence of the medium disappears.

This is important in deciding *what* the object is that we are supposed to see. In the daytime, practically all the light that reaches the eye comes ultimately from the sun, but we do not say that we are seeing only the sun. We are seeing the last region after which the course of the light was virtually unimpeded until it reached the eye. When light is reflected or scattered, we consider, as a rule, that it makes us see the last object from which it is reflected or scattered; when it is refracted, we consider that we are still seeing the previous source, though inaccurately. Reflected light, however, is not always taken as giving perception of the reflector; it is not so taken when the reflection is accurate, as in a mirror. What I see when I shave I consider to be my own face. But when sunlight is reflected on an outdoor landscape it gives me much more information about the things in the landscape than about the sun, and I therefore consider that I am perceiving the things in the landscape.

In a lesser degree similar things may be said about sound. We distinguish between hearing a sound and hearing an echo of it. If the sun were as chromatically noisy as it is bright, and if terrestrial things were resonant only to certain of its notes, we should say that we were hearing the things, not the sun, when they gave characteristic sound reflections.

The other senses do not give the same kind of perception of distant objects or of intermediate links in causal chains, because they are not concerned with physical processes having the peculiar kind of independence that is characteristic of wave motions.

From what we have been saying it is clear that the relation of a percept to the physical object which is supposed to be perceived is vague, approximate, and somewhat indefinite. There is no *precise* sense in which we can be said to perceive physical objects.

The question of perception as a source of knowledge can be merged in a wider question: How far, and in what circumstances, can one stage in a physical process be a basis for inferring an earlier stage? Clearly this can only happen in so far as the process in question is independent of other processes. That processes can be thus independent is perhaps surprising. We see the separate stars because the light that starts from each travels on through regions full of other trails of light, and yet retains its independence. When this independence fails, we see a vague blur, like the Milky Way. In the case of the Milky Way, the independence does not fail till we reach the physiological stage; that is why telescopes can separate the different stars of the Milky Way. But the independence of the light from different parts of one star cannot be restored by telescopes; that is why stars have no measurable apparent magnitude.

Our perceptive apparatus, as studied by the physiologist, can to some extent be ignored by the physicist, because it can be treated as approximately constant. It is not, of course, really constant. By squinting I can see two suns, but I do not imagine that I have performed an astronomical miracle. If I close my eyes and turn my face to the sun, I see a vague red glare; this change in the sun's appearance I attribute to myself, not to the sun. Things look different when I see them out of the corner of my eye from what they do when I focus on them. They look different to short-sighted and to long-sighted people. And so on. But common sense learns to distinguish these subjective sources of variation in the percept from those that are due to variation in the physical objects. Until we learn to draw, we think that a rectangular object always looks rectangular; and we are right, in the sense that an animal inference causes us to judge it to be rectangular.

Sciences deal with these matters by assuming a normal observer who is to some extent a fiction, like the economic man, but not so completely a fiction as to be practically useless. When a normal observer sees a difference between two objects—for example, that one looks yellow and the other looks blue—this difference is assumed to have its source in a difference in the objects, not in the subjective perceptive apparatus of the observer. If, in a given case, this assumption is erroneous, it is held that multiplicity of observations by a multitude of observers will correct it. By such methods, the physicist is enabled to treat our perceptive apparatus as the source of a *constant* error, which, because it is constant, is for many purposes negligible.

The principles which justify the inference from percepts to physical objects have not been sufficiently studied. Why, for example, when a number of people see the sun, should we believe that there is a sun outside their percepts, and not merely that there are laws determining the circumstances in which we shall have the experience called "seeing the sun"?

Here we come up against a principle which is used both by science and by common sense, to the effect that, when a number of phenomena in separated parts of space-time are obviously causally interconnected, there must be some continuous process in the intervening regions which links them all together. This principle of spatio-temporal continuity needs to be re-examined after we have considered the inference from perceptual to physical space. In the meantime, it can be accepted as at least a first step toward formalizing inference from perceptual physical objects.

I will conclude with a summary of the present chapter.

Our main question was: If physics is true, how can it be known, and what, besides physics, must we know to infer physics? This problem arises through the physical causation of perception, which makes it probable that physical objects differ greatly from percepts; but if so, how can we infer physical objects from percepts? Moreover, since perceiving is considered to be "mental" while its causes are "physical," we are confronted with the old problem of the relation between mind and matter. My own belief is that the "mental" and the "physical" are not so disparate as is generally thought. I should define a "mental" occurrence as one which someone knows otherwise than by inference; the distinction between "mental" and "physical" therefore belongs to theory of knowledge, not to metaphysics.

One of the difficulties which have led to confusion was failure to distinguish between perceptual and physical space. Perceptual space consists of perceptible relations between parts of percepts, whereas physical space consists of inferred relations between inferred physical things. What I see may be outside my percept of my body, but not outside my body as a physical thing.

Percepts, considered causally, are between events in afferent nerves (stimulus) and events in efferent nerves (reaction); their location in causal chains is the same as that of certain events in the brain. Percepts as a source of knowledge of physical objects can only serve their purpose in so far as there are separable, more or less independent, causal chains in the physical world. This only happens approximately, and therefore the inference from percepts to physical objects cannot be precise. Science consists largely of devices for overcoming this initial lack of precision on the assumption that perception gives a first approximation to the truth.

CHAPTER TWO

Structure

In the present chapter we shall be concerned with a purely logical discussion which is essential as a preliminary to any further steps in the interpretation of science. The logical concept which I shall endeavor to explain is that of "structure."

To exhibit the structure of an object is to mention its parts and the ways in which they are interrelated. If you were learning anatomy, you might first learn the names and shapes of the various bones, and then be taught where each bone belongs in the skeleton. You would then know the structure of the skeleton in so far as anatomy has anything to say about it. But you would not have come to an end of what can be said about structure in relation to the skeleton. Bones are composed of cells, and cells of molecules, and each molecule has an atomic structure which it is the business of chemistry to study. Atoms, in turn, have a structure which is studied in physics. At this point orthodox science ceases its analysis, but there is no reason to suppose that further analysis is impossible. We shall have occasion to suggest the analysis of physical entities into structures of events, and even events, as I shall try to show, may be regarded with advantage as having a structure.

Let us consider next a somewhat different example of structure, namely sentences. A sentence is a series of words, arranged

From *Human Knowledge* by Bertrand Russell, Part IV, Chapter III, pp. 250-256. Copyright 1948 by Bertrand Russell. Reprinted by permission of the publishers, George Allen & Unwin Ltd., London, and Simon and Schuster, Inc., New York.

in order by the relation of earlier and later if the sentence is spoken, and of left to right if it is written. But these relations are not really between words; they are between *instances* of words. A word is a class of similar noises, all having the same meaning or nearly the same meaning. (For simplicity I shall confine myself to speech as opposed to writing.) A sentence also is a class of noises, since many people can utter the same sentence. We must say, then, not that a sentence is a temporal series of words but that a sentence is a class of noises, each consisting of a series of noises in quick temporal succession, each of these latter noises being an instance of a word. (This is a necessary but not a sufficient characteristic of a sentence; it is not sufficient because some series of words are not significant.) I will not linger on the distinction between different parts of speech, but will go on to the next stage in analysis, which belongs no longer to syntax but to phonetics. Each instance of a word is a complex sound, the parts being the separate letters (assuming a phonetic alphabet). Behind the phonetic analysis there is a further stage: the analysis of the complex physiological process of uttering or hearing a single letter. Behind the physiological analysis is the analysis of physics, and from this point onward analysis proceeds as in the case of the bones.

In the above account I passed hastily over two points that need elucidation, namely, that words have *meaning* and sentences have *significance*. "Rain" is a word, but "raim" is not, though both are classes of similar noises. "Rain is falling" is a sentence, but "rain snow elephant" is not, though both are series of words. To define "meaning" and "significance" is not easy, as we saw in discussing the theory of language. The attempt is not necessary so long as we confine ourselves strictly to questions of structure. A word acquires meaning by an external relation, just as a man acquires the property of being an uncle. No post-mortem, however thorough, will reveal whether the man was an uncle or not, and no analysis of a set of noises (so long as everything external to them is excluded) will show whether this set of noises has meaning, or significance if the set is a series of what seem to be words.

The above example illustrates that an analysis of structure, however complete, does not tell you all that you may wish to know about an object. It tells you only what are the parts of the object and how they are related to each other; it tells you nothing about the relations of the object to objects that are not parts or components of it.

The analysis of structure usually proceeds by successive stages, as in both the above examples. What are taken as unanalyzed units in one stage are themselves exhibited as complex structures in the next stage. The skeleton is composed of bones, the bones of cells, and cells of molecules, the molecules of atoms, the atoms of electrons, positrons, and neutrons; further analysis is as yet conjectural. Bones, molecules, atoms, and electrons may each be treated, for certain purposes, as if they were unanalyzable units devoid of structure, but at no stage is there any positive reason to suppose that this is in fact the case. The ultimate units so far reached may at any moment turn out to be capable of analysis. Whether there must be units incapable of analysis because they are destitute of parts is a question which there seems no way of deciding. Nor is it important, since there is nothing erroneous in an account of structure which starts from units that are afterward found to be themselves complex. For example, points may be defined as classes of events, but that does not falsify anything in traditional geometry, which treated points as simples. Every account of structure is relative to certain units which are, for the time being, treated as if they were devoid of structure, but it must never be assumed that these units will not, in another context, have a structure which it is important to recognize.

There is a concept of "identity of structure" which is of great importance in relation to a large number of questions. Before giving a precise definition of this concept, I will give some preliminary illustrations of it.

Let us begin with linguistic illustrations. Suppose that in any given sentence you substitute other words, but in a way which still leaves the sentence significant; then the new sentence has the same structure as the original one. Suppose, e.g., you start with "Plato loved Socrates"; for "Plato" substitute "Brutus," for "loved" substitute "killed," and for "Socrates" substitute "Caesar." You thus arrive at the sentence "Brutus killed Caesar," which has the same structure as "Plato loved Socrates." All sentences having this structure are called "dyadic-relation sentences." Similarly from "Socrates is Greek" you could have passed to "Brutus is Roman" without change of structure; sentences having this structure are called "subject-predicate sentences." In this way sentences can be classified by their structure; there are in theory an infinite number of structures that sentences may have.

Logic is concerned with sentences that are true in virtue of their structure, and that always remain true when other words are substituted, so long as the substitution does not destroy significance. Take, for example, the sentence: "If all men are mortal and Socrates is a man, then Socrates is mortal." Here we may substitute other words for "Socrates," "man," and "mortal" without destroying the truth of the sentence. It is true that there are other words in the sentence, namely, "if-then" (which must count as one word), "all," "are," "and," "is," "a." These words must not be changed. But these are "logical" words, and their purpose is to indicate structure; when they are changed, the structure is changed. (All this raises problems, but it is not necessary for our present purpose to go into them.) A sentence belongs to logic if we can be sure that it is true (or that it is false) without having to know the meanings of any of the words except those that indicate structure. That is the reason for the use of variables. Instead of the above sentence about Socrates and man and mortal, we say, "If all a's are β's and κ is an a, then κ is a β." Whatever κ and a and β may be, this sentence is true; it is true in virtue of its structure. It is in order to make this clear that we use "κ" and "a" and "β" instead of ordinary words.

Let us take next the relation of a district to a map of it. If the district is small, so that the curvature of the earth can be neglected, the principle is simple: east and west are represented by right and left, north and south by up and down, and all distances are reduced in the same proportion. It follows that from every statement about the map you can infer one about the district, and vice versa. If there are two towns, A and B, and the map is on the scale of an inch to the mile, then from the fact that the mark "A" is ten inches from the mark "B" you can infer that A is ten miles from B, and conversely; and from the direction of the line from the mark "A" to the mark "B" you can infer the direction of the line from A to B. These inferences are possible owing to identity of structure between the map and the district.

Now take a somewhat more complicated illustration: the relation of a gramophone record to the music that it plays. It is obvious that it could not produce this music unless there were a certain identity of structure between it and the music, which can be exhibited by translating sound relations into space relations, or vice versa; e.g., what is nearer to the center on the record corresponds to what is later in time in the music. It is only because of the identity of structure that the record is able to cause the music. Very similar considerations apply to telephones, broadcasting, etc.

We can generalize such examples so as to deal with the relations of our perceptual experiences to the external world. A wireless set transforms electromagnetic waves into sound waves; a human organism transforms sound waves into auditory sensations. The electromagnetic waves and the sound waves have a certain similarity of structure, and so (we may assume) have the sound waves and the auditory sensations. Whenever one complex structure causes another, there must be much the same structure in the cause and in the effect, as in the case of the gramophone record and the music. This is plausible if we accept the maxim "Same cause, same effect" and its consequence, "Different effects, different causes." If this principle is regarded as valid, we can infer from a complex sensation or series of sensations the structure of its physical cause, but nothing more, except that relations of neighborhood must be preserved; i.e., neighboring causes have neighboring effects. This argument is one which needs much amplification; for the moment I am merely mentioning it by way of anticipation, in order to show one of the important applications of the concept of structure.

We can now proceed to the formal definition of "structure." It is to be observed that structure always involves relations: a mere class, as such, has no structure. Out of the terms of a given class many structures can be made, just as many different sorts of houses can be made out of a given heap of bricks. Every relation has what is called a "field," which consists of all the terms that have the relation to something or to which something has the relation. Thus the field of "parent" is the class of parents and children, and the field of "husband" is the class of husbands and wives. Such relations have two terms, and are called "dyadic." There are also relations of three terms, such as jealousy and "between"; these are called "triadic." If I say "A bought B from C for D pounds," I am using a "tetradic" relation. If I say "A minds B's love for C more than D's hatred of E," I am using a "pentadic" relation. To this series of kinds of relation there is no theoretical limit.

Let us in the first instance confine ourselves to dyadic relations. We shall say that a class a ordered by the relation R has the same structure as a class β ordered by the relation S, if to every term in a some one term in β corresponds, and vice versa, and if when two terms in a have the relation R, then the corresponding terms in β have the relation S, and vice versa. We may illustrate by the similarity between a spoken and a written sentence. Here the class of spoken words in the sentence is a, the class of written words in the sentence is β, and if one spoken word is earlier than another, then the written word corresponding to the one is to the left of the written word corresponding to the other (or to the right if the language is Hebrew). It is in consequence of this identity of structure that spoken and written sentences can be translated into each other. The process of learning to read and write is the process of learning which spoken word corresponds to a given written word and vice versa.

A structure may be defined by several relations. Take, for instance, a piece of music. One note may be earlier or later than another, or simultaneous with it. One note may be louder than another, or higher in pitch, or differing through a wealth or poverty of harmonics. All the relations of this kind that are

musically relevant must have analogues in a gramophone record
if it is to give a good reproduction. In saying that the record
must have the same structure as the music, we are not concerned
with only one relation R between the notes of the music and
one corresponding relation S between the corresponding marks
on the record, but with a number of relations such as R and a
number of corresponding relations such as S. Some maps use
different colors for different altitudes; in that case, different positions on the map correspond to different latitudes and longitudes, while different colors correspond to different elevations.
The identity of structure in such maps is greater than in others;
that is why they are able to give more information.

The definition of identity of structure is exactly the same for
relations of higher order as it is for dyadic relations. Given, for
example, two triadic relations R and S, and given two classes α
and β of which α is contained in the field of R while β is contained in the field of S, we shall say that α ordered by R has the
same structure as β ordered by S if there is a way of correlating
one member of α to one of β, and vice versa, so that, if a_1, a_2, a_3
are correlated respectively with b_1, b_2, b_3, if R relates a_1, a_2, a_3
(in that order), then S relates b_1, b_2, b_3 (in that order), and vice
versa. Here, again, there may be several relations such as R, and
several such as S; in that case, there is identity of structure in
various respects.

When two complexes have the same structure, every statement
about the one, in so far as it depends only on structure, has a
corresponding statement about the other, true if the first was
true, and false if the first was false. Hence arises the possibility of
a dictionary, by means of which statements about the one complex can be translated into statements about the other. Or, instead of a dictionary, we may continue to use the same words,
but attach different meanings to them according to the complex
to which they are referred. This sort of thing happens in interpreting a sacred text or the laws of physics. The "days" in the
Biblical account of the Creation are taken to mean "ages," and
in this way Genesis is reconciled with geology. In physics, assuming that our knowledge of the physical world is only as to

the structure resulting from the empirically known relation of "neighborhood" in the topological sense, we have immense latitude in the interpretation of our symbols. Every interpretation that preserves the equations and the connection with our perceptive experiences has an equal claim to be regarded as *possibly* the true one, and may be used with equal right by the physicist to clothe the bare bones of his mathematics.

Take, for example, the question of waves versus particles. Until recently it was thought that this was a substantial question: light must consist either of waves or of little packets called photons. It was regarded as unquestionable that matter consisted of particles. But at last it was found that the equations were the same if both matter and light consisted of particles, or if both consisted of waves. Not only were the equations the same, but all the verifiable consequences were the same. Either hypothesis, therefore, is equally legitimate, and neither can be regarded as having a superior claim to truth. The reason is that the physical world can have the same structure, and the same relation to experience, on the one hypothesis as on the other.

Considerations derived from the importance of structure show that our knowledge, especially in physics, is much more abstract and much more infected with logic than it used to seem. There is, however, a very definite limit to the process of turning physics into logic and mathematics; it is set by the fact that physics is an empirical science, depending for its credibility upon relations to our perceptive experiences. The further development of this theme must be postponed until we come to the theory of scientific inference.

CHAPTER THREE

Time and Space

The purpose of this [chapter] is to provide possible interpretations of the concepts of science, in terms of possible minimum vocabularies. It will not be asserted that no other interpretations are possible, but it is hoped that in the course of the discussion certain common characteristics of all acceptable interpretations will emerge. In the present [part] we shall be concerned to interpret the word "time."

Most people will be inclined to agree with St. Augustine: "What, then, is time? If no one asks of me, I know; if I wish to explain to him who asks, I know not." Philosophers, of course, have learned to be glib about time, but the rest of mankind, although the subject feels familiar, are apt to be aware that a few questions can reduce them to hopeless confusion. "Does the past exist? No. Does the future exist? No. Then only the present exists? Yes. But within the present there is no lapse of time? Quite so. Then time does not exist? Oh, I wish you wouldn't be so tiresome." Any philosopher can elicit this dialogue by a suitable choice of interlocuter.

Sir Isaac Newton, who understood the Book of Daniel, also knew all about time. Let us hear what he has to say on the subject in the Scholium following the initial definitions in the *Principia*:

The first part of this chapter is from Bertrand Russell, *Human Knowledge*, Part IV, Chapter V, pp. 266-272. Copyright 1948 by Bertrand Russell. Reprinted by permission of the publishers, George Allen & Unwin Ltd., London, and Simon and Schuster, Inc., New York.

"I do not define time, space, place, and motion, as being well-known to all. Only I must observe, that the vulgar conceive those quantities under no other notions but from the relation they bear to sensible objects. And thence arise certain prejudices, for the removal of which, it will be convenient to distinguish them into absolute and relative, true and apparent, mathematical and common. Absolute, true, and mathematical time, of itself, and from its own nature flows equably without regard to anything external, and by another name is called duration: relative, apparent, and common time, is some sensible external (whether accurate or unequable) measure of duration by the means of motion, which is commonly used instead of true time; such as an hour, a day, a month, a year."

He goes on to explain that days are not all of equal length, and that perhaps there is nowhere in nature a truly uniform motion, but that we arrive at absolute time, in astronomy, by correction of "vulgar" time.

Sir Isaac Newton's "absolute" time, although it remained embedded in the technique of classical physics, was not generally accepted. The theory of relativity has provided reasons, within physics, for its rejection, though these reasons leave open the possibility of absolute space-time. But before relativity Newton's absolute time was already widely repudiated, though for reasons which had nothing to do with physics. Whether, before relativity, these reasons had any validity is a question which I think we shall find it worth while to examine.

Although Newton says that he is not going to define time because it is well known, he makes it clear that only "vulgar" time is well known, and that mathematical time is an inference. In modern terms, we should rather call it an adjustment than an inference. The process of arriving at "mathematical" time is essentially as follows: There are a number of periodic motions—the rotations and revolutions of the earth and the planets, the tides, the vibrations of a tuning fork, the heart beats of a healthy man at rest—which are such that if one of them is assumed to be uniform, all the others are approximately uniform. If we take one of them, say the earth's rotation, as uniform by definition, we can arrive at physical laws—notably the law of gravitation—which explain the phenomena, and show why the other periodic motions are approximately uniform. But unfortunately the laws so established are only approximate, and, what is more, they show that the earth's rotation should suffer retardation by tidal friction. This is self-contradictory if the earth's rotation is taken as the measure of time; we therefore seek a different measure, which shall also make our physical laws approximate more nearly to exact truth. It is found convenient not to take any actual motion as *defining* the measure of time, but to adopt a compromise measure which makes physical laws as accurate as possible. It is this compromise measure that serves the purposes for which Newton invoked "absolute" time. There is no reason, however, to suppose that it represents a physical reality, for the choice of a measure of time is conventional, like the choice between the Christian and the Mohammedan eras. We choose, in fact, the measure which gives the greatest attainable simplicity to the statement of physical laws, but we do so on grounds of convenience, not because we think that this measure is more "true" than any other.

A frequent ground of objection to Newton's "absolute" time has been that it could not be observed. This objection, on the face of it, comes oddly from men who ask us to believe in electrons and protons and neutrons, quantum transitions in atoms, and what not, none of which can be observed. I do not think that physics can dispense with inferences that go beyond observation. The fact that absolute time cannot be observed is not, by itself, fatal to the view that it should be accepted; what is fatal is the fact that physics can be interpreted without assuming it. Whenever a body of symbolic propositions which there is reason to accept can be interpreted without inferring such-and-such unobserved entities, the inference from the body of propositions in question to these supposed entities is invalid, since, even if there are no such entities, the body of propositions may be true. It is on this ground, and not merely because "absolute" time cannot be observed, that Newton was mistaken in inferring it from the laws of physics.

While the rejection of Newton's view is a commonplace, few people seem to realize the problems that it raises. In physics there is an independent variable t, the values of which are supposed to form a continuous series, and each to be what is commonly called an "instant." Newton regarded an instant as a physical reality, but the modern physicist does not. Since, however, he continues to use the variable t, he must find some interpretation for its values, and the interpretation must serve the technical purposes that were served by Newton's "absolute" time. This problem of the interpretation of "t" is the one that concerns us in this chapter. In order to simplify the approach to it, we will at first ignore relativity and confine ourselves to time as it appears in classical physics.

We shall continue to give the name "instant" to a value of the variable t, but we shall look for an interpretation of the word "instant" in terms of physical data; that is to say, we shall expect the word to have a definition, and not to belong to a minimum physical vocabulary. All that we require of the definition is that instants, so defined, should have the formal properties demanded of them by mathematical physics.

In seeking a definition of "instant" or "point," the material to be used depends upon the theory we adopt as to "particulars" or proper names. We may take the view that when, for instance, a given shade of color appears in two separated locations, there are two separate "particulars," each of which is an "instance" of the shade of color, and is a subject of which qualities can be predicated, but which is not defined by its qualities, since another precisely similar particular might exist elsewhere. Or we may take the view that a "particular" is a bundle of co-existing qualities. The discussions of the preceding chapter, as well as the earlier discussion of proper names, inclined us to the latter view. I shall, however, in this and the two following chapters, hypothetically adopt the former view, and in Chapter VIII I shall show how to interpret what has been said in terms of the latter view.[1] For the moment, therefore, I take as raw material

---

[1] [This discussion is not included here. Russell developed the further analysis of "event" in *An Inquiry into Meaning and Truth* (1940), of which a concise statement is given in *Human Knowledge*, Part IV, Chapter VIII. This analysis, however, is merely superimposed upon the treatment in terms of events and does not supersede the latter.]

"events," which are to be imagined as each occupying a finite continuous portion of space-time. It is assumed that two events can overlap, and that no event recurs.

It is clear that time is concerned with the relation of earlier and later; it is generally held also that nothing of which we have experience has a merely instantaneous existence. Whatever is earlier or later than something else I shall call an "event." We shall want our definition of "instant" to be such that an event can be said to exist "at" certain instants and not at certain others. Since we have agreed that events, so far as known to us, are not merely instantaneous, we shall wish to define "instant" in such a way that every event exists at a continuous stretch of the series of instants. That instants must form a series defined by means of the relation of earlier and later is one of the requisites that our definition must fulfill. Since we have rejected Newton's theory, we must not regard instants as something independent of events, which can be occupied by events as hats occupy hat pegs. We are thus compelled to search for a definition which makes an instant a structure composed of a suitable selection of events. Every event will be a member of many such structures, which will be the instants during which it exists: it is "at" every instant which is a structure of which the event is a member.

A date is fixed with complete precision if it is known concerning every event in the world whether it wholly preceded that date, or will wholly come after it, or was in existence at that date. To this statement someone might object that if the world were to remain without change for, say, five minutes, there would be no way of fixing a date within these five minutes if the above view were adopted, for every event wholly preceding one part of the five minutes would wholly precede every other part, every event wholly subsequent to any part of the five minutes would be wholly subsequent to every other part, and every event existing at any part of the five minutes would exist throughout the whole of them. This, however, is not an objection to our statement, but only to the supposition that time could go on in an unchanging world. On the Newtonian theory this would be possible, but on a relational theory of time it be-comes self-contradictory. If time is to be defined in terms of events, it must be impossible for the universe to be unchanging for more than an instant. And when I say "impossible," I mean *logically* impossible.

Although we cannot agree with Newton that "time" does not need to be defined, it is obvious that temporal statements de-mand *some* undefined terms. I choose the relation of earlier-and-later, or of wholly-preceding. Between two events *a* and *b* three temporal relations are possible: *a* may be wholly before *b*, or *b* may be wholly before *a*, or *a* and *b* may overlap. Suppose you wish to fix as accurately as possible some date within the dura-tion of *a*. If you say that your date is also to be within the dura-tion of *b*, you fix the date somewhat more accurately than by merely saying that it is within the duration of *a*, unless it so happens that *a* and *b* both began and ended together. Suppose now there is a third event *c* which overlaps with both *a* and *b;* that is to say, in ordinary language (to which we are not yet entitled), there is a period of time during which *a* and *b* and *c* all exist. This period, in general, will be shorter than that dur-ing which both *a* and *b* exist. We now look for a fourth event *d* which overlaps with *a* and *b* and *c*—i.e., in ordinary language, exists during some part of the time during which *a* and *b* and *c* all exist; the time during which *a* and *b* and *c* and *d* all exist is, in general, shorter than that during which any three of them all exist. In this way, step by step, we get nearer to an exact date.

Let us suppose this process carried on as long as possible, i.e., until there is no event remaining which overlaps with all the events already in our group. I say that when this stage has been reached, the group of events that has been constructed may be defined as an "instant." To prove that this assertion is legiti-mate I only have to show that "instants," so defined, have the mathematical properties that physics demands. I do not have to show that this is what people commonly mean when they speak of "instants," though it might be desirable to complete the argument by showing that they commonly mean nothing.

An "instant," as I propose to define the term, is a class of events having the following two properties: (1) all the events in the class overlap; (2) no event outside the class overlaps with every member of the class. This group of events, as I shall show, does not persist for a finite time.

To say that an event persists for a finite time can only mean, on a relational view of time, that changes occur while it exists, i.e., that the events which exist when it begins are not all identical with the events existing when it ends. This amounts to saying that there are events which overlap with the given event but not with each other. That is to say: "*a* lasts for a finite time" means "There are two events *b* and *c* such that each overlaps with *a* but *b* wholly precedes *c*."

We may apply the same definition to a group of events. If the members of the group do not all overlap, the group as a whole has no duration, but if they all overlap we shall say that the group as a whole lasts for a finite time if there are at least two events which overlap with every member of the group although one of them wholly precedes the other. If this is the case, change occurs while the group persists; if not, not. Now, if a group constitutes an "instant" as above defined, no event outside the group overlaps all the members of the group, and no event inside the group wholly precedes any other event inside the group. Therefore the group as a whole does not last for a finite time. And therefore it may suitably be defined as an "instant."

Instants will form a series ordered by a relation defined in terms of the relation "wholly preceding" among events. One instant is earlier than another if there is a member of the first instant which wholly precedes a member of the second, i.e., if some event "at" the first instant wholly precedes some event "at" the second instant. It will be observed that being "at" an instant is the same thing as being a member of the class which is the instant.

According to the above definition, it is logically impossible for the world to remain unchanging throughout a finite time. If two instants differ, they are composed (at least in part) of

different members, and that means that some event existing at
the one instant does not exist at the other.

In this [part] we shall be concerned with space as it appears
in classical physics.[1] That is to say, we shall be concerned to find
an "interpretation" (not necessarily the only possible one) for
the geometrical terms used in physics. Much more complicated
and difficult problems arise in regard to space than in regard
to time. This is partly because of problems introduced by relativity. For the present, however, we will ignore relativity, and
treat space as separable from time after the manner of pre-Ein-
steinian physics.

For Newton, space, like time, was "absolute"; that is to say,
it consisted of a collection of points, each devoid of structure,
and each one of the ultimate constituents of the physical world.
Each point was everlasting and unchanging; change consisted
in its being "occupied" sometimes by one piece of matter, sometimes by another, and sometimes by nothing. As against this
view, Leibniz contended that space was only a system of relations, the terms of the relations being material and not merely
geometrical points. Although both physicists and philosophers
tended more and more to take Leibniz's view rather than Newton's, the technique of mathematical physics continued to be
Newtonian. In the mathematical apparatus, "space" is still an
assemblage of "points," each defined by three co-ordinates, and
"matter" is an assemblage of "particles," each of which occupies
different points at different times. If we are not to agree with
Newton in ascribing physical reality to points, this system requires some interpretation in which "points" have a structural
definition.

I have used the word "physical reality," which may be held
to savor too much of metaphysics. What I mean can be ex-

1 [The remainder of this chapter is from *Human Knowledge* by Bertrand
Russell, Part IV, Chapter VI, pp. 277-281. Copyright 1948 by Bertrand
Russell. Reprinted by permission of the publishers, George Allen & Unwin
Ltd., London, and Simon and Schuster, Inc., New York.]

pressed, in a form more acceptable to modern taste, by means of the technique of minimum vocabularies. Given a collection of names, it may happen that some of the things named have a structural definition in terms of others; in that case, there will be a minimum vocabulary not containing the names for which definitions can be substituted. For example, every French human being has a proper name, and "the French nation" may also be regarded as a proper name, but it is an unnecessary one, since we can say, "The French nation" is defined as "the class consisting of the following individuals (here follows the list)." Such a method is only applicable to finite classes, but there are other methods not subject to this limitation. We can define "France" by its geographical boundaries, and then define "French" as "born in France."

To this process of substituting structural definitions for names there are obviously limits in practice, and perhaps (though this may be questioned) there are also limits in theory. Assuming, for the sake of simplicity, that matter consists of electrons and protons, we could, in theory, give a proper name to each electron and each proton; we could then define an individual human being by mentioning the electrons and protons composing his body at various times; thus names for individual human beings are theoretically superfluous. Speaking generally, whatever has a discoverable structure does not need a name, since it can be defined in terms of the names of its ingredients and the words for their relations. On the other hand, whatever has no known structure needs a name if we are to be able to express all our knowledge concerning it.

It is to be observed that a denotational definition does not make a name superfluous. E.g., "the father of Alexander the Great" is a denotational definition, but does not enable us to express the fact which contemporaries could have expressed by "That is Alexander's father," where "that" functions as a name.

When we deny Newton's theory of absolute space, while continuing to use what we call "points" in mathematical physics, our procedure is only justified if there is a structural definition of "point" and (in theory) of particular points. Such a definition must proceed by methods similar to those that we employed in defining "instants." This, however, is subject to two provisos: first, that our manifold of points is to be three-dimensional, and second, that we have to define a point at an instant. To say that a point P at one time is identical with a point Q at another time is to say something which has no definite meaning except a conventional one which depends upon a choice of material axes. As this matter has to do with relativity, I shall not consider it further at present, but shall confine myself to the definition of points at a given instant, ignoring the difficulties connected with the definition of simultaneity.

In what follows I lay no stress on the particular method of constructing points that I have adopted. Other methods are possible, and some of these may be preferred. What is important is only that such methods can be devised. In defining instants, we used the relation of "overlapping" in a temporal sense—a relation which holds between two events when (in ordinary language) there is a time during which both exist. In defining points, we use the relation of "overlapping" in a spatial sense, which is to subsist between two simultaneous events that (in ordinary language) occupy the same region of space in whole or in part. It is to be observed that events, unlike pieces of matter, are not to be thought of as mutually impenetrable. The impenetrability of matter is a property which results tautologically from its definition. "Events," however, are only defined as terms not assumed to possess a structure, and having spatial and temporal relations such as belong to finite volumes and finite periods of time. When I say "such as," I mean "similar as regards logical properties." But "overlapping" is not itself to be defined logically; it is an empirically known relation, having, in the construction which I advocate, only an ostensive definition.

In a manifold of more than one dimension, we cannot construct anything having the properties required of "points" by

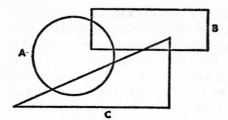

means of a two-term relation of "overlapping." As the simplest illustration, let us take areas on a plane. Three areas, A, B, C, on a plane may each overlap with the other two, without there being any region common to all three. In the accompanying figure, the circle A overlaps with the rectangle B and the triangle C, and B overlaps with C, but there is no region common to A and B and C. The basis of our construction will have to be a relation of *three* areas, not of two. We shall say that three areas are "copunctual" when there is a region common to all three. (This is an explanation, not a definition.)

We shall assume that the areas with which we are concerned are all either circles, or such shapes as can result from circles by stretching or compressing in a manner which leaves them oval. In that case, given three areas A, B, C which are copunctual, and a fourth area D such that A, B, D are copunctual and also A, C, D and B, C, D, then A, B, C, D all have a common region.

We now define a group of any number of areas as "copunctual" if every triad chosen out of the group is copunctual. A copunctual group of areas is a "point" if it cannot be enlarged without ceasing to be copunctual, i.e., if, given any area X outside the group, there are in the group at least two areas A and B such that A, B, X are not copunctual.

This definition is only applicable in two dimensions. In three dimensions, we must start with a relation of copunctuality between *four* volumes, and the volumes concerned must all be either spheres or such oval volumes as can result from spheres by continuous stretching in some directions and compressing in others. Then, as before, a copunctual group of volumes is one in which every four are copunctual, and a copunctual group is a "point" if it cannot be enlarged without ceasing to be copunctual.

In n dimensions the definitions are the same, except that the original relation of copunctuality has to be between $n + 1$ regions.

"Points" are defined as classes of events by the above methods, with the tacit assumption that every event "occupies" a more or less oval region.

"Events" are to be taken, in the present discussion, as the undefined raw material from which geometrical definitions are to be derived. In another context we may have to inquire as to what can be meant by an "event," and we may then be able to carry analysis a step further, but for the present we regard the manifold of "events," with their spatial and temporal relations, as empirical data.

The way in which spatial order results from our assumptions is somewhat complicated. I shall say nothing about it here, as I have dealt with it in *The Analysis of Matter*, where, also, there is a much fuller discussion of the definition of "points" (Chapters XXVIII and XXIX).[1]

1 [Cf. above, page 68, note.]

CHAPTER FOUR

Space-Time

Everybody knows that Einstein substituted space-time for space and time, but people unfamiliar with mathematical physics have usually only a very vague conception as to the nature of the change. As it is an important change in relation to our attempts to conceive the structure of the world, I shall try, in this chapter, to explain those parts of it that have philosophical importance.

Perhaps the best starting point is the discovery that "simultaneity" is ambiguous when applied to events in different places. Experiments, especially the Michelson-Morley experiment, led to the conclusion that the velocity of light is the same for all observers, however they may be moving. This seemed, at first sight, to be a logical impossibility. If you are in a train which is moving at 30 miles an hour, and you are passed by a train which is moving at 60 miles an hour, its speed relatively to you will be 30 miles an hour. But if it is moving with the velocity of light, its speed relatively to you will be the same as its speed relatively to fixed points on the earth. Beta particles sometimes move with speeds up to 90 per cent of the velocity of light, but if a physicist could move with such a particle and be passed by a light ray, he would still judge that the light was moving, relatively to him, at the same rate as if he were at rest in relation

From *Human Knowledge* by Bertrand Russell, Part IV, Chapter VII, pp. 287-291. Copyright 1948 by Bertrand Russell. Reprinted by permission of the publishers, George Allen & Unwin Ltd., London, and Simon and Schuster, Inc., New York.

to the earth. This paradox is explained by the fact that different observers, all equipped with perfect chronometers, will form different estimates of time intervals and different judgments as to simultaneity in different places.

It is not difficult to see the necessity for such differences when once it has been pointed out. Suppose an astronomer observes an event in the sun, and notes the time of his observation; he will infer that the event happened about eight minutes before his observation, since that is the length of time that it takes light to travel from the sun to the earth. But now suppose that the earth were traveling very fast toward the sun or away from it. Unless you already knew at what moment, by terrestrial time, the event on the sun took place, you would not know how far the light had had to travel, and therefore your observation would not enable you to know when the event in the sun had taken place. That is to say, there would be no definite answer to the question: What events on earth were simultaneous with the solar event that you had observed?

From the ambiguity of simultaneity it follows that there is a parallel ambiguity in the conception of distance. If two bodies are in relative motion, their distance apart is continually changing, and in pre-relativity physics there was supposed to be such a quantity as their "distance at a given instant." But if there is ambiguity as to what is the same instant for the two bodies, there is also ambiguity as to "distance at a given instant." One observer will form one estimate, and another will form another, and there is no reason to prefer either estimate. In fact, neither time intervals nor spatial distances are facts independent of the movements of the observer's body. There is a kind of subjectivity about measurements of time and space separately—not a psychological but a physical subjectivity, since it affects instruments, not only mental observers. It is like the subjectivity of the camera, which takes a photograph from a certain point of view. Photographs from other points of view would look different, and no one among them would have a claim to special accuracy.

There is, however, one relation between two events which is

the same for all observers. Formerly there were two, distance in space and lapse of time, but now there is only one, which is called "interval." It is because there is only this one relation of interval, instead of distance and lapse of time, that we have to substitute the one concept of space-time for the two concepts of space and time. But although we can no longer separate space and time, there are still two kinds of interval, one spacelike and the other timelike. The interval is spacelike if a light signal, sent out by the body on which one event occurs, reaches the body on which the other event occurs after this other event has taken place. (It is to be observed that there is no ambiguity about the time-order of events on a given body.) It is timelike if a light signal sent out from one event reaches the body on which the other event occurs before this other event has taken place. Since nothing travels faster than light, we may say that the interval is timelike when one event may have an effect upon the other, or upon something in the same space-time region as the other; when this is not possible, the interval is spacelike.

In the special theory of relativity the definition of "interval" is simple; in the general theory it is more complicated.

In the special theory, suppose that an observer, treating himself as motionless, judges the distance between two events to be r, and the lapse of time between them to be t. Then if c is the velocity of light, the square of the interval is

$$c^2 t^2 - r^2$$

if it is timelike, while if it is spacelike it is

$$r^2 - c^2 t^2$$

It is usually simpler technically to take it as always one of these, in which case the square of the other sort of interval is negative, and the interval is imaginary.

When neither gravitation nor electromagnetic forces are involved, it is found that the interval, as above defined, is the same for all observers, and may therefore be regarded as a genuine physical relation between the two events.

The general theory of relativity removes the above restriction by introducing a modified definition of "interval."

In the general theory of relativity there is no longer a definite "interval" between distant events, but only between events that are very near together. At a great distance from matter the formula for interval approximates to that in the special theory, but elsewhere the formula varies according to the nearness of matter. It is found that the formula can be so adjusted as to account for gravitation, assuming that matter which is moving freely moves in a geodesic; i.e., chooses the shortest or longest route from any one point to a neighboring point.

It is assumed that, independently of interval, space-time points have an order, so that, along any route, one point can be between two others which are near it. For example, the interval between two different points on one light ray is zero, but the points still have a temporal order: if a ray travels outward from the sun, the parts near the sun are earlier than the parts farther from it. The space-time order of events is presupposed in the assignment of co-ordinates, for although this is to a great extent conventional it must always be such that neighboring points have co-ordinates that do not differ much, and that, as points approach closer to each other, the difference between their co-ordinates approaches zero as a limit.

If the physical world is held to consist of a four-dimensional manifold of events, instead of a manifold of persistent moving particles, it becomes necessary to find a way of defining what is meant when we say that two events are part of the history of one and the same piece of matter. Until we have such a definition, "motion" has no definite meaning, since it consists in one thing being in different places at different times. We must define a "particle," or material point, as a series of space-time points having to each other a causal relation which they do not have to other space-time points. There is no difficulty of principle about this procedure. Dynamical laws are habitually stated on the assumption that there are persistent particles, and are used to decide whether two events A and B belong to the biography of one particle or not. We merely retain the laws, and turn the statement that A and B belong to the same biography into a definition of a "biography," whereas before it seemed to be a substantial assertion.

This point perhaps needs some further explanation. Starting from the assumption that there are persistent pieces of matter, we arrive at physical laws connecting what happens to a piece of matter at one time with what happens to it at another. (The most obvious of such laws is the law of inertia.) We now state these laws in a different way: we say that given an event of a certain kind in a certain small region of space-time, there will be neighboring events in neighboring regions which will be related to the given event in certain specific ways. We say that a series of events related to each other in these specific ways is to be called one piece of matter at different times. Thus matter and motion cease to be part of the fundamental apparatus of physics. What is fundamental is the four-dimensional manifold of events, with various kinds of causal relations. There will be relations making us regard the events concerned as belonging to one piece of matter, others making us regard them as belonging to different but interacting pieces of matter, others relating a piece of matter to its "empty" environment (e.g., emission of light), and yet others relating events that are both in empty space, e.g., parts of one light ray.

The collecting of events into series such as will secure the persistence of matter is only partially and approximately possible. When an atom is pictured as a nucleus with planetary electrons, we cannot say, after a quantum transition, that such-and-such an electron in the new state is to be identified with such-and-such an electron in the old state. We do not even know for certain that the number of electrons in the universe is constant. Mass is only a form of energy, and there is no reason why matter should not be dissolved into other forms of energy. It is energy, not matter, that is fundamental in physics. We do not define energy; we merely discover laws as to the changes in its distribution. And these laws are no longer such as to determine a unique result where atomic phenomena are concerned, though macroscopic occurrences remain statistically determinate with an enormously high degree of probability.

The continuity of space-time, which is technically assumed in physics, has nothing in its favor except technical convenience. It may be that the number of space-time points is finite, and that space-time has a granular structure, like a heap of sand. Provided the structure is fine enough, there will be no observable phenomenon to show that there is not continuity. Theoretically, there might be evidence against continuity, but there could never be conclusive evidence in its favor.

The theory of relativity does not affect the space and time of perception. My space and time, as known in perception, are correlated with those that, in physics, are appropriate to axes that move with my body. Relatively to axes tied to a given piece of matter, the old separation of space and time still holds; it is only when we compare two sets of axes in rapid relative motion that the problems arise which the theory of relativity solves. Since no two human beings have a relative velocity approaching that of light, comparison of their experiences will reveal no such discrepancies as would result if airplanes could move as fast as beta particles. In the psychological study of space and time, therefore, the theory of relativity may be ignored.

CHAPTER FIVE

Space-Time and Causality

Physical events are arranged by physics in a four-dimensional manifold called space-time. This manifold is an improvement on the older manifold of "things" arranged in varying spatial patterns at varying times; and this, in turn, was an improvement upon the manifold resulting from assuming an accurate correspondence between percepts and "things." No doubt physics would like to forget its early history, which, like that of many established institutions, is not so creditable as could be wished. But unfortunately its title to our allegiance is difficult to disentangle from its early association with naïve realism; even in its most sophisticated form, it still appears as an emendation, for which naïve realism supplies the text.

Perceptual space is a common-sense construction, composed of diverse raw materials. There are visual space-relations: up-and-down, right-and-left, depth up to a certain distance (after which differences of depth become imperceptible). There are the differences in sensations of touch which enable us to distinguish a touch on one part of the body from a touch on another. There is the somewhat vague power of estimating the direction of a sound. Then there are experienced correlations, of which the most important is the correlation of sight and

From *Human Knowledge* by Bertrand Russell, Part IV, Chapter X, pp. 319-332. Copyright 1948 by Bertrand Russell. Reprinted by permission of the publishers, George Allen & Unwin Ltd., London, and Simon and Schuster, Inc., New York.

touch; there are observations of movement, and the experience of moving parts of our own body.

Out of such raw materials (the above list does not claim to be complete) common sense constructs a single space containing objects perceived and unperceived, the perceived objects being identified with percepts, according to the principles of naïve realism. The unperceived objects, for common sense, are those which we should perceive if we were in the right position and with suitably adjusted sense organs, together with objects only perceived by others, and objects, such as the interior of the earth, which are perceived by no one but inferred by common sense.

In the passage from the common-sense world to that of physics, certain common-sense assumptions are retained, though in a modified form. For instance, we assume that the furniture of our room continues to exist when we do not see it. Common sense supposes that what continues is just what we see when we look, but physics says that what continues is the external cause of what we see, i.e., a vast assemblage of atoms undergoing frequent quantum transformations. In the course of these transformations they radiate energy, which, when it comes in contact with a human body, has various effects, some of which are called "perceptions." Two simultaneous parts of one visual percept have a certain visual spatial relation which is a component of the total percept; the physical objects which correspond to these parts of my total percept have a relation roughly corresponding to this visual spatial relation. When I say that the relation "corresponds," I mean that it is part of a system of relations having, to some extent, the same geometry as that of visual percepts, and that the location of physical objects in physical space has discoverable relations to the location of perceptual objects in perceptual space.

But this correspondence is by no means exact. Let us take, to simplify our problem, the heavenly bodies as they are and as they appear. As they appear, they do not obviously differ as regards distance from us; they look like bright points or patches on the celestial sphere. That is to say, their position in visual space is defined by only two co-ordinates. But eclipses and occultations soon led to the view that they are not in fact all equidistant from the earth, though it was a long time before differences of distance among the fixed stars were admitted. To fix the position of a heavenly body relatively to ourselves we need three polar co-ordinates, r, θ, ϕ. It was assumed that θ and ϕ could be the same for the physical star as for the perceived star, but r must be computed; in fact a great deal of astronomy has been concerned with computing r. The assumption that θ and ϕ are the same in visual and physical space is equivalent to the assumption that light travels in straight lines. This assumption, after a time, came to be thought not exactly true, but it is still sufficiently true for a first approximation.

The θ and ϕ of astronomical space, though they have approximately the same numerical measure as the θ and ϕ of visual space, are not identical with the latter. If they were identical, the hypothesis that light does not move exactly in straight lines would be meaningless. This illustrates at once the connection and the difference between visual space when we look at the night sky and astronomical space as constructed by the astronomers. The connection is kept as close as may be, but beyond a point it has to be abandoned if we are to believe in comparatively simple laws governing the real and apparent movements of the heavenly bodies.

Small distances from ourselves are not estimated by the elaborate methods required in astronomy. We can roughly "see" small distances, though the stereoscope produces this effect deceptively. We judge things that touch our body to be close to the part they touch. When things are not touching us, we sometimes can move so as to come in contact with them; the amount of movement required measures, roughly, their initial distance from us. We have thus three common-sense ways of estimating the distance of visual objects on the surface of the earth. Scientific ways of estimating distance use these ways as their foundation, but correct them by means of physical laws inferred by assuming them. The whole process is one of tinkering. If common-sense estimates of distances and sizes are roughly correct, then certain physical laws are roughly correct. If these laws are quite correct, the common-sense estimates must be slightly amended. If the various laws are not exactly compatible, they must be adjusted until the inconsistency ceases. Thus observation and theory interact; what, in scientific physics, is called an observation is usually something involving a considerable admixture of theory.

Let us now abandon the consideration of the stages toward theoretical physics, and compare the finished physical world with the world of common sense. I see, let us suppose, a buttercup and a bluebell; common sense says the buttercup is yellow and the bluebell is blue. Physics says that electromagnetic waves of many different frequencies start from the sun and reach the two flowers; when they reach them, the buttercup scatters the waves whose frequency produces a yellow sensation, and the bluebell those that produce a blue sensation. This difference in the effect of the two flowers is assumed to be due to some difference in their structure. Thus although yellow and blue exist only where there is an eye, the difference between them allows us to infer differences between the physical objects in the directions in which we see yellow and blue respectively.

Common sense constructs a single space containing "things" which combine properties revealed by different senses, such as hot and hard and bright. These "things" are placed by common sense in a three-dimensional space, in which distance cannot be estimated by common-sense methods unless it is small. Physics until recently retained something like "things," but called it "matter," and robbed it of all properties except position in space. The position of a piece of matter in space was roughly identical with that of the corresponding "thing," except that the distance, if great, had to be calculated by rather elaborate scientific methods.

In this picking and choosing among common-sense beliefs, physics has acted without formulated principles, but nevertheless on a subconscious plan which we must try to make explicit. Part of this plan is to retain always as much of the common-sense world as is possible without intolerable complication; another part is to make such non-refutable assumptions as will lead to simple causal laws. This latter procedure is already implicit in the common-sense belief in "things": we do not believe that the visible world ceases to exist when we shut our eyes, and we hold that the cat exists when it is secretly stealing the cream as well as when we are punishing it for doing so. All this is "probable" inference: it is logically possible to suppose that the world consists only of my percepts, and the inference to the common-sense world, as to that of physics, is non-demonstrative. But I do not wish to go behind common sense at present; I wish only to consider the transition from common sense to physics.

Modern physics is further from common sense than the physics of the nineteenth century. It has dispensed with matter, substituting series of events; it has abandoned continuity in microscopic phenomena; and it has substituted statistical averages for strict deterministic causality affecting each individual occurrence. But it has still retained a great deal of which the source is common sense. And there are still continuity and determinism so far as macroscopic phenomena are concerned, and for most purposes there is still matter.

The world of physics contains more than the world of percepts, and in some respects contains more than the world of common sense. But while it exceeds both in quantity, it falls short of both in known qualitative variety. Both common sense and physics supplement percepts by the assumption that things do not cease to exist when unperceived, and by the further assumption that things never perceived can often be inferred. Physics supplements the common-sense world by the whole theory of microscopic phenomena; what it asserts about atoms and their history surpasses what common sense allows itself to infer.

There are two specially important kinds of chains of events: first, those which constitute the history of a given piece of matter; second, those which connect an object with the perception of it. The sun, for instance, has a biography consisting of all that happens in the part of space-time that it occupies; this biography may be said to *be* the sun. It also emits radiations, some of which reach eyes and brains and cause the sort of occurrence which is called "seeing the sun." Broadly speaking, the former set of events consists of quantum transitions, the latter of radiant energy. There are correspondingly two sets of causal laws, one set connecting events belonging to the same piece of matter, the other connecting parts of the same radiation. There is also a third set of laws, concerning the transition from energy in the atom to radiant energy and vice versa.

Perceiving, as we know it introspectively, appears to be something quite different from the events that physics considers. Therefore if there is to be inference from percepts to physical occurrences, or from physical occurrences to percepts, we need laws which, prima facie, are not physical. I incline to think that physics *can* be so interpreted as to include these laws, but for the present I shall not consider this possibility. Our problem is, therefore: Taking percepts as we know them in experience, and physical occurrences as asserted by physics, what laws do we know that interconnect the two and therefore allow inference from one to the other?

In part the answer is already patent to common sense. We see when light strikes the eye, we hear when sound strikes the ear, we have sensations of touch when the body is in contact with something else, and so on. These laws are not laws of physics or physiology, unless physics is subjected to a radical reinterpretation. They are laws stating the physical antecedents of perceptions. These antecedents are partly outside the percipient's body (except when he is perceiving something in his own body), partly in his sense organs and nerves, partly in his brain. A failure in any of these antecedents prevents the perception. But conversely, if one of the later antecedents is caused in an unusual way, the percept will be what it would have been if the causation had been usual, and the percipient is liable to be deceived—for example, by something seen in a mirror or heard on the wireless, if he is unaccustomed to mirrors and wireless.

Each single inference from a perception to a physical object is therefore liable to be erroneous in the sense of causing expectations that are not fulfilled. It will not *usually* be erroneous in this sense, since the habit of making that sort of inference must have been generated by a number of occasions when the inference was justified. But here a little further precision is necessary. From a practical point of view, an inference from a percept is justified if it gives rise to expectations that are verified. This, however, is all within the realm of percepts. All that strictly follows is that our inferences as to physical objects are consistent with experience, but there may be other hypotheses that are equally consistent.

The justification of our inferences from perception to physical objects depends upon the consistency of the whole system. First, from ordinary perceptions, we arrive at an elementary kind of physics; this suffices to cause us to put in a separate category dreams, mirages, etc., which contradict our elementary physics. We then set to work to improve our elementary physics so as to include the exceptional phenomena; there is, for instance, a perfectly good physical theory of mirages. We learn in this way to be critical, and we form the concept of a "trained observer." We are critical of percepts in the name of laws, and of laws in the name of percepts; gradually, as physics improves, a closer and closer harmony between percepts and laws is established.

But when I say that we become critical of percepts, I must guard against a misunderstanding. Percepts certainly occur, and a theory which has to deny any of them is faulty; but some, being caused in an unusual way, lead common sense into erroneous inferences. Of this the mirage is a good example. If I see a lake which is only a mirage, I see what I see just as truly as if there were a physical lake; I am mistaken not as to the percept but as to what it implies. The percept makes me think that if I walk in a certain direction, I shall reach water that I can drink, and in this I am deceived; but my visual percept may be exactly what it would be if there really were water. My physics, if adequate, must explain not only that there is no water but also why there seems to be water. A mistaken perception is mistaken not as to the percept itself but as to its causal correlates and antecedents and consequents; frequently the mistake is in an animal inference. The fact that animal inferences may be mistaken is one reason for classifying them as inferences.

The relation of physical laws to experience is not altogether simple. Broadly speaking, laws can be disproved by experience, but not proved by it. That is to say, they assert more than experience alone would warrant. In the case of the mirage, if I have believed it real, and have also assumed that a large lake will not dry up in a few hours, I can discover that the mirage caused me to have a false belief. But the false belief may have been the belief that the lake could not dry up so quickly. The belief in the persistence of material objects throughout the interval between two occasions when they are observed is one which, as a matter of logic, cannot be proved by observation. Suppose I were to set up the hypothesis that tables, whenever no one is looking, turn into kangaroos; this would make the laws of physics very complicated, but no observation could refute it. The laws of physics, in the form in which we accept them, must not only be in agreement with observation, but must, as regards what is not observed, have certain characteristics of simplicity and continuity which are not empirically demonstrable. In general, we think that physical phenomena are not affected by being observed, although this is not thought to be strictly true as regards the minute phenomena upon which quantum theory is based.

Physics, assuming it perfected, would have two characteristics. In the first place, it would be able to predict percepts; no perception would be contrary to what physics had led us to expect. In the second place, it would assume unobserved physical occurrences to be governed by causal laws as similar as possible to those that we infer from cases of continuous observation. For example, if I watch a moving body, the motion that I see is sensibly continuous; I therefore assume that all motion, whether observed or not, is approximately continuous.

This brings us to the question of causal laws and physical space-time. Physical space-time, as we have seen, is an inference

from perceptual space and time; it contains all observed occurrences, and also all unobserved occurrences. But since it is inferential, the location of an occurrence in it is also inferential.
The locating of events in physical space-time is effected by two
methods. First, there is a correlation between perceptual space
and time and physical space-time, though this correlation is
only rough and approximate. Second, the causal laws of physics
assign an order to the events concerned, and it is partly by
means of them that unobserved events are located in space-time.

A causal law, as I use the term, is any law which, if true, makes
it possible, given a certain number of events, to infer something
about one or more other events. For example, "Planets move
in ellipses" is a causal law. If this law is true, since five points
determine an ellipse, five data (theoretically) should enable us
to calculate the orbit of the planet. Most laws, however, have
not this simplicity; they are usually expressed in differential
equations. When they are so expressed they assume an order:
each event must have four co-ordinates, and neighboring events
are those whose co-ordinates are very nearly the same. But the
question arises: How do we assign co-ordinates to events in
physical space-time? I maintain that, in doing so, we make use
of causal laws. That is to say, the relation of causal laws to space-
time order is a reciprocal one. The correct statement is: Events
can be arranged in a four-dimensional order such that when
so arranged they are interconnected by causal laws which are
approximately continuous, i.e., events whose co-ordinates differ
very little also differ very little. Or rather: Given any event,
there is a series of closely similar events, in which the time co-
ordinate varies continuously from rather less to rather more
than that of the given event, and in which the space co-ordinates
vary continuously about those of the given event. This principle, apparently, does not hold for quantum transitions, but
it holds for macroscopic events, and for all events (such as light
waves) where there is no matter.

The correlation between physical and perceptual space-time,
which is only approximate, proceeds as follows: In visual space,
if objects are near enough for differences of depth to be per-

ceptible, every visual percept has three polar co-ordinates, which may be called distance, up-and-downness, and right-and-leftness. All these are qualities of the percept, and all are measurable. We may assign the same numerical co-ordinates to the physical object which we are said to be seeing, but these co-ordinates no longer have the same meaning as they have in visual space. It is because they do not have the same meaning that it is possible for the correlation to be only rough—for example, if the object is seen through a refracting medium. But although the correlation is rough, it is very useful in establishing a first approximation to the co-ordinates of events in physical space-time. The subsequent corrections are effected by means of causal laws, of which the refraction of light may again serve as an example.

There is no logical reason why there should be such causal laws, or known relations establishing such a four-dimensional order among events. The usual argument for the acceptance of physical laws is that they are the simplest hypotheses hitherto devised that are consistent with observation wherever observation is possible. They are not, however, the only hypotheses consistent with observation. Nor is it clear by what right we objectify our preference for *simple* laws.

What physics says about the world is much more abstract than it seems to be, because we imagine that its space is what we know in our own experience, and that its matter is the kind of thing that feels hard when we touch it. In fact, even assuming physics true, what we know about the physical world is very little. Let us first consider theoretical physics in the abstract, and then in relation to experience.

As an abstract system, physics, at present, says something like this: There is a manifold, called the manifold of events, which has a system of relations among its terms by means of which it acquires a certain four-dimensional geometry. There is an extra-geometrical quantity called "energy," which is unevenly distributed throughout the manifold, but of which some finite amount exists in every finite volume. The total of energy is constant. The laws of physics are laws as to the changes in the distribution of energy. To state these laws, we have to distinguish two kinds of regions—those that are called "empty" and those that are said to contain "matter." There are very small material systems called "atoms"; each atom may contain any one of a certain discrete denumerable series of amounts of energy. Sometimes it suddenly parts with a finite amount of energy to the non-material environment; sometimes it suddenly absorbs a finite amount from the environment. The laws as to these transitions from one energy level to another are only statistical. In a given period of time, if not too short, there will be, in a given state of the environment, a calculable number of transitions of each possible kind, the smaller transitions being commoner than the greater.

In "empty space" the laws are simpler and more definite. Parcels of energy that leave an atom spread outward equally in all directions, traveling with the velocity of light. Whether a parcel travels in waves or in little units or in something which is a combination of both is a matter of convention. Everything proceeds simply until the radiant energy hits an atom, and then the atom may absorb a finite amount of it, with the same individual indeterminacy and statistical regularity as applies to the emission of energy by atoms.

The amount of energy emitted by an atom in a given transition determines the "frequency" of the radiant energy that results. And this in turn determines the kinds of effects that the radiant energy can have upon any matter that it may encounter. "Frequency" is a word associated with waves, but if the wave theory of light is discarded "frequency" may be taken as a measurable but undetermined quality of a radiation. It is measurable by its effects.

So much for theoretical physics as an abstract logical system. It remains to consider how it is connected with experience.

Let us begin with the geometry of space-time. We assume that the position of a point in space-time can be determined by four real numbers, called co-ordinates; it is also generally supposed, though this is not essential, that to every set of four real numbers as co-ordinates (if not too great) a position in space-time corresponds. It will simplify exposition to adopt this supposition. If we do, the number of positions in space-time is the same as the number of real numbers, which is called c. Now of every class of c entities we can assert every kind of geometry in which there is a one-one correspondence between a position and a finite ordered set of real numbers (co-ordinates). Therefore to specify the geometry of a manifold tells us nothing unless the ordering relation is given. Since physics is intended to give empirical truth, the ordering relation must not be a purely logical one, such as might be constructed in pure mathematics, but must be a relation defined in terms derived from experience. If the ordering relation is derived from experience, the statement that space-time has such-and-such a geometry is one having a substantial empirical content, but if not, not.

I suggest that the ordering relation is contiguity or compresence, in the sense in which we know these in sensible experience. Something must be said about these.

Contiguity is a property given in sight and touch. Two portions of the visual field are contiguous if their apparent distances and their angular co-ordinates (up-and-down, right-and-left) differ very little. Two parts of my body are contiguous if the qualities by which I locate a touch in the two parts differ very little. Contiguity is quantitative, and therefore enables us to make series of percepts: If A and B and C are contiguous, but B is more contiguous to both A and C than they are to each other, B is to be put between A and C. There is also contiguity in time. When we hear a sentence, the first and second words are more contiguous than the first and third words. In this way, by means of spatial and temporal contiguity, our experiences can be arranged in an ordered manifold. We may assume that this ordered manifold is a part of the ordered manifold of physical events, and is ordered by the same relation.

For my part, however, I prefer the relation of "compresence." If we use this relation, we suppose that every event occupies a finite amount of space-time; that is to say, no event is confined to a point of space or an instant of time. Two events are said to be "compresent" when they overlap in space-time; this is the definition for abstract physics. But we need, as we saw, a definition derived from experience. As an ostensive definition from experience I should give the following: Two events are "compresent" when they are related in the way in which two simultaneous parts of one experience are related. At any given moment, I am seeing certain things, hearing others, touching others, remembering others, and expecting yet others. All these percepts, recollections, and expectations are happening to me now; I shall say that they are mutually "compresent." I assume that this relation, which I know in my own experience, can also hold between events that are not experienced, and can be the relation by which space-time order is constructed. This will have as a consequence that two events are compresent when they overlap in space-time, which, if space-time order is taken as already determined, may serve, *within physics*, as the definition of compresence.

Compresence is not the same thing as simultaneity, though it implies it. Compresence, as I mean it, is to be taken as known through experience, and having only an ostensive definition. Nor should I define "compresence" as "simultaneity in one person's experience." I should object to this definition on two grounds: first, that it could not be extended to physical occurrences experienced by no one; second, that "experience" is a vague word. I should say that an event is "experienced" when it gives rise to a habit, and that broadly speaking this only happens if the event occurs where there is living matter. If this is correct, "experience" is not a fundamental concept.

The question now arises: Can we construct space-time order out of compresence alone, or do we need something further? Let us take a simplified hypothesis. Suppose there are n events, $a_1, a_2, \ldots a_n$, and suppose a_1 is compresent only with a_2, a_2 is compresent with a_1 and a_3, a_3 with a_2 and a_4, and so on. We can then construct the order $a_1, a_2, \ldots a_n$. We shall say that an event is "between" two others if it is compresent with both, but they are not compresent with each other; and, more generally, if a, b, c are three different events, we shall say that b is "between" a and c if the events compresent with both a and c are a proper part of the events compresent with *b*. This may be taken as the definition of "between." Supplemented by suitable axioms, it will generate the kind of order we want.

It should be observed that we cannot construct space-time order out of Einstein's relation of "interval." The interval between two parts of a light ray is zero, and yet we have to distinguish between a light ray that goes from A to B and one that goes from B to A. This shows that "interval" alone does not suffice.

If the above point of view is adopted, points in space-time become classes of events. I have dealt with this subject in *The Analysis of Matter* and in Chapters [III and IV] of this Part, and will therefore say no more about it.

So much for the definition of space-time order in terms of experience. It remains to restate the connection of physical events in the outer world with percepts.

When energy emitted by matter as a result of quantum transitions travels, without further quantum transitions, to a given part of a human body, it sets up a train of quantum transitions which ultimately reach the brain. Assuming the maxim "Same cause, same effect," with its consequence, "Different effects, different causes," it follows that if two trains of radiant energy, falling on the same point of the body, cause different percepts, there must be differences in the two trains, and therefore in the quantum transitions that gave rise to them. Assuming the existence of causal laws, this argument seems unobjectionable, and gives a basis for the inference from perceptions to the material source of the process by which they are caused.

I think—though I say this with hesitation—that the distinction between spatial and temporal distance requires the consideration of causal laws. That is to say, if there is a causal law connecting an event A with an event B, then A and B are separated in time, and it is a matter of convention whether we shall also consider them separated in space. There are, however, some difficulties about this view. A number of people may hear or see something simultaneously, and in this case there is a causal connection with no time interval. But in such a case the connection is indirect, like that connecting brothers or cousins; that is to say, it travels first from effect to cause and then from cause to effect. But how are we to distinguish cause from effect before we have established the time order? Eddington says we do so by means of the second law of thermodynamics. In a spherical radiation, we take it that it travels *from* a center, not *to* it. But I, since I wish to connect physics with experience, should prefer to say that we establish time order by means of memory and our immediate experience of temporal succession. What is remembered is, by definition, in the past; and there are earlier and later within the specious present. Anything compresent with something remembered, but not with my present experience, is also in the past. From this starting point we can extend the definition of time order, and the distinction of past and future, step by step to all events. We can then distinguish cause from effect, and say that causes are always earlier than effects.

According to the above theory, there are certain elements that are carried over unchanged from the world of sense to the world of physics. These are: the relation of compresence, the relation of earlier and later, some elements of structure and differences in certain circumstances, i.e., when we experience different sensations belonging to the same sense, we may assume that their causes differ. This is the residue of naïve realism that survives in physics. It survives primarily because there is no positive argument against it, because the resulting physics fits the known facts, and because prejudice causes us to cling to naïve realism wherever it cannot be disproved. Whether there are any better reasons than these for accepting physics remains to be examined.

PART FOUR

PART FOUR

Psychology

In his writings on psychology one of Russell's main points
of emphasis is that of maintaining that it is unnecessary
to accept the existence of any uniquely 'mental' entity. He
opposes dualistic views that divide the world into 'mind'
and 'matter,' as well as idealist ones that maintain that
'mind' is fundamental. He found that the general pattern
of interpretation he had employed for the physical sciences
could be applied to 'mental' terms as well. Russell had
resolved physical things at first into groups of sense data,
and later into groups of events. Mental terms, he found,
could be similarly resolved.

The interpretation of terms for both physical objects
and mental phenomena by means of sense data or events
provides, Russell believes, an alternative metaphysics to
either dualism or idealism. It is a version of 'neutral monism,' which resolves the antithesis between matter and
mind by finding a 'neutral' entity to be ultimate in the
universe. In the interpretation of science given in Part Two
the 'neutral' entities are sense data, and mental phenomena can be shown to be arrangements of sense data. In the
view of science given in Part Three the neutral entities are

events, and mental phenomena, like physical, are resolved into events.

Chapter One, from *The Analysis of Mind* (1921), is representative of his earlier period. His later writings state very similar views; as an example the reader is referred to *Human Knowledge*, Part One, Chapter Six.

CHAPTER ONE

Mental Phenomena

At the end of our journey it is time to return to the question
from which we set out, namely: What is it that characterizes
mind as opposed to matter? Or, to state the same question in
other terms: How is psychology to be distinguished from physics? The answer provisionally suggested at the outset of our
inquiry was that psychology and physics are distinguished by
the nature of their causal laws, not by their subject matter. At
the same time we held that there is a certain subject matter,
namely images, to which only psychological causal laws are
applicable; this subject matter, therefore, we assigned exclusively to psychology. But we found no way of defining images
except through their causation; in their intrinsic character they
appeared to have no universal mark by which they could be
distinguished from sensations.

In this last lecture I propose to pass in review various suggested methods of distinguishing mind from matter. I shall
then briefly sketch the nature of that fundamental science
which I believe to be the true metaphysic, in which mind and
matter alike are seen to be constructed out of a neutral stuff,
whose causal laws have no such duality as that of psychology,
but form the basis upon which both physics and psychology
are built.

From *The Analysis of Mind* by Bertrand Russell (1921), Lecture XV (Conclusion), pp. 287-308. Reprinted by permission of the publisher, George
Allen & Unwin Ltd., London. Russell's references to earlier chapters in the
original work have been retained.

In search for the definition of "mental phenomena," let us begin with "consciousness," which is often thought to be the essence of mind. In the first lecture I gave various arguments against the view that consciousness is fundamental, but I did not attempt to say what consciousness is. We must find a definition of it, if we are to feel secure in deciding that it is not fundamental. It is for the sake of the proof that it is not fundamental that we must now endeavour to decide what it is.

"Consciousness," by those who regard it as fundamental, is taken to be a character diffused throughout our mental life, distinct from sensations and images, memories, beliefs and desires, but present in all of them.[1] Dr. Henry Head, in an article which I quoted in Lecture III, distinguishing sensations from purely physiological occurrences, says: "Sensation, in the strict sense of the term, demands the existence of consciousness" (p. 184). This statement, at first sight, is one to which we feel inclined to assent, but I believe we are mistaken if we do so. Sensation is the sort of thing of which we *may* be conscious, but not a thing of which we *must* be conscious. We have been led, in the course of our inquiry, to admit unconscious beliefs and unconscious desires. There is, so far as I can see, no class of mental or other occurrences of which we are always conscious whenever they happen.

The first thing to notice is that consciousness must be *of* something. In view of this, I should define "consciousness" in terms of that relation of an image or a word to an object which we defined, in Lecture XI, as "meaning." When a sensation is followed by an image which is a "copy" of it, I think it may be said that the existence of the image constitutes consciousness of the sensation, provided it is accompanied by that sort of belief which, when we reflect upon it, makes us feel that the image is a "sign" of something other than itself. This is the sort of belief which, in the case of memory, we expressed in the words "this occurred"; or which, in the case of a judgment of perception, makes us believe in qualities correlated with present sensations, as e.g., tactile and visual qualities are correlated.

[1] Cf. Lecture VI.

The addition of some element of belief seems required, since mere imagination does not involve consciousness of anything, and there can be no consciousness which is not of something. If images alone constituted consciousness of their prototypes, such imagination-images as in fact have prototypes would involve consciousness of them; since this is not the case, an element of belief must be added to the images in defining consciousness. The belief must be of that sort that constitutes objective reference, past or present. An image, together with a belief of this sort concerning it, constitutes, according to our definition, consciousness of the prototype of the image.

But when we pass from consciousness of sensations to consciousness of objects of perception, certain further points arise which demand an addition to our definition. A judgment of perception, we may say, consists of a core of sensation, together with associated images, with belief in the present existence of an object to which sensation and images are referred in a way which is difficult to analyse. Perhaps we might say that the belief is not fundamentally in any *present* existence, but is of the nature of an expectation: for example, when we see an object, we expect certain sensations to result if we proceed to touch it. Perception, then, will consist of a present sensation together with expectations of future sensations. (This, of course, is a reflective analysis, not an account of the way perception appears to unchecked introspection.) But all such expectations are liable to be erroneous, since they are based upon correlations which are usual but not invariable. Any such correlation may mislead us in a particular case, for example, if we try to touch a reflection in a looking glass under the impression that it is "real." Since memory is fallible, a similar difficulty arises as regards consciousness of past objects. It would seem odd to say that we can be "conscious" of a thing which does not or did not exist. The only way to avoid this awkwardness is to add to our definition the proviso that the beliefs involved in consciousness must be *true*.

In the second place, the question arises as to whether we can be conscious of images. If we apply our definition to this case, it seems to demand images of images. In order, for example, to be conscious of an image of a cat, we shall require, according to the letter of the definition, an image which is a copy of our image of the cat, and has this image for its prototype. Now, it hardly seems probable, as a matter of observation, that there are images of images, as opposed to images of sensations. We may meet this difficulty in two ways, either by boldly denying consciousness of images, or by finding a sense in which, by means of a different accompanying belief, an image, instead of meaning its prototype, can mean another image of the same prototype.

The first alternative, which denies consciousness of images, has already been discussed when we were dealing with Introspection in Lecture VI. We then decided that there must be, in some sense, consciousness of images. We are therefore left with the second suggested way of dealing with knowledge of images. According to this second hypothesis, there may be two images of the same prototype, such that one of them means the other, instead of meaning the prototype. It will be remembered that we defined meaning by association: a word or image means an object, we said, when it has the same associations as the object. But this definition must not be interpreted too absolutely: a word or image will not have *all* the same associations as the object which it means. The word "cat" may be associated with the word "mat," but it would not happen except by accident that a cat would be associated with a mat. And in like manner an image may have certain associations which its prototype will not have, e.g. an association with the word "image." When these associations are active, an image means an image, instead of meaning its prototype. If I have had images of a given prototype many times, I can mean one of these, as opposed to the rest, by recollecting the time and place or any other distinctive association of that one occasion. This happens, for example, when a place recalls to us some thought we previously had in that place, so that we remember a thought as opposed to the occurrence to which it referred. Thus we may say that we think of an image A when we have a similar image B associated with recollections of circumstances connected with

A, but not with its prototype or with other images of the same prototype. In this way we become aware of images without the need of any new store of mental contents, merely by the help of new associations. This theory, so far as I can see, solves the problems of introspective knowledge, without requiring heroic measures such as those proposed by Knight Dunlap, whose views we discussed in Lecture VI.

According to what we have been saying, sensation itself is not an instance of consciousness, though the immediate memory by which it is apt to be succeeded is so. A sensation which is remembered becomes an object of consciousness as soon as it begins to be remembered, which will normally be almost immediately after its occurrence (if at all); but while it exists it is not an object of consciousness. If, however, it is part of a perception, say of some familiar person, we may say that the person perceived is an object of consciousness. For in this case the sensation is a *sign* of the perceived object in much the same way in which a memory-image is a sign of a remembered object. The essential practical function of "consciousness" and "thought" is that they enable us to act with reference to what is distant in time or space, even though it is not at present stimulating our senses. This reference to absent objects is possible through association and habit. Actual sensations, in themselves, are not cases of consciousness, because they do not bring in this reference to what is absent. But their connection with consciousness is very close, both through immediate memory, and through the correlations which turn sensations into perceptions.

Enough has, I hope, been said to show that consciousness is far too complex and accidental to be taken as the fundamental characteristic of mind. We have seen that belief and images both enter into it. Belief itself, as we saw in an earlier lecture, is complex. Therefore, if any definition of mind is suggested by our analysis of consciousness, images are what would naturally suggest themselves. But since we found that images can only be defined causally, we cannot deal with this suggestion, except in connection with the difference between physical and psychological causal laws.

I come next to those characteristics of mental phenomena

which arise out of mnemic causation. The possibility of action with reference to what is not sensibly present is one of the things that might be held to characterize mind. Let us take first a very elementary example. Suppose you are in a familiar room at night, and suddenly the light goes out. You will be able to find your way to the door without much difficulty by means of the picture of the room which you have in your mind. In this case visual images serve, somewhat imperfectly it is true, the purpose which visual sensations would otherwise serve. The stimulus to the production of visual images is the desire to get out of the room, which, according to what we found in Lecture III, consists essentially of present sensations and motor impulses caused by them. Again, words heard or read enable you to act with reference to the matters about which they give information; here, again, a present sensible stimulus, in virtue of habits formed in the past, enables you to act in a manner appropriate to an object which is not sensibly present. The whole essence of the practical efficiency of "thought" consists in sensitiveness to *signs*: the sensible presence of A, which is a sign of the present or future existence of B, enables us to act in a manner appropriate to B. Of this, words are the supreme example, since their effects as signs are prodigious, while their intrinsic interest as sensible occurrences on their own account is usually very slight.

The operation of signs may or may not be accompanied by consciousness. If a sensible stimulus A calls up an image of B, and we then act with reference to B, we have what may be called consciousness of B. But habit may enable us to act in a manner appropriate to B as soon as A appears, without ever having an image of B. In that case, although A operates as a sign, it operates without the help of consciousness. Broadly speaking, a very familiar sign tends to operate directly in this manner, and the intervention of consciousness marks an imperfectly established habit.

The power of acquiring experience, which characterizes men and animals, is an example of the general law that, in mnemic causation, the causal unit is not one event at one time, but two or more events at two or more times.[1] A burnt child fears the fire, that is to say, the neighbourhood of fire has a different effect upon a child which has had the sensations of burning than upon one which has not. More correctly, the observed effect, when a child which has been burnt is put near a fire, has for its cause, not merely the neighbourhood of the fire, but this together with the previous burning. The general formula, when an animal has acquired experience through some event A, is that, when B occurs at some future time, the animal to which A has happened acts differently from an animal to which A has not happened. Thus A and B together, not either separately, must be regarded as the cause of the animal's behaviour, unless we take account of the effect which A has had in altering the animal's nervous tissue, which is a matter not patent to external observation except under very special circumstances. With this possibility, we are brought back to causal laws, and to the suggestion that many things which seem essentially mental are really neural. Perhaps it is the nerves that acquire experience rather than the mind. If so, the possibility of acquiring experience cannot be used to define mind.[1]

Very similar considerations apply to memory, if taken as the essence of mind. A recollection is aroused by something which is happening now, but is different from the effect which the present occurrence would have produced if the recollected event had not occurred. This may be accounted for by the physical effect of the past event on the brain, making it a different instrument from that which would have resulted from a different experience. The causal peculiarities of memory *may*, therefore, have a physiological explanation. With every special class of mental phenomena this possibility meets us afresh. If psychology is to be a separate science at all, we must seek a wider ground for its separateness than any that we have been considering hitherto.

We have found that "consciousness" is too narrow to characterize mental phenomena, and that mnemic causation is too wide. I come now to a characteristic which, though difficult to

1 Cf. Lecture IV.

define, comes much nearer to what we require, namely subjectivity.

Subjectivity, as a characteristic of mental phenomena, was considered in Lecture VII, in connection with the definition of perception. We tnere decided that those particulars which constitute the physical world can be collected into sets in two ways, one of which makes a bundle of all those particulars that are appearances of a given thing from different places, while the other makes a bundle of all those particulars which are appearances of different things from a given place. A bundle of this latter sort, at a given time, is called a "perspective"; taken throughout a period of time, it is called a "biography." Subjectivity is the characteristic of perspectives and biographies, the characteristic of giving the view of the world from a certain place. We saw in Lecture VII that this characteristic involves none of the other characteristics that are commonly associated with mental phenomena, such as consciousness, experience and memory. We found in fact that it is exhibited by a photographic plate, and, strictly speaking, by any particular taken in conjunction with those which have the same "passive" place in the sense defined in Lecture VII. The particulars forming one perspective are connected together primarily by simultaneity; those forming one biography, primarily by the existence of direct time-relations between them. To these are to be added relations derivable from the laws of perspective. In all this we are clearly not in the region of psychology, as commonly understood; yet we are also hardly in the region of physics. And the definition of perspectives and biographies, though it does not yet yield anything that would be commonly called "mental," is presupposed in mental phenomena, for example in mnemic causation: the causal unit in mnemic causation, which gives rise to Semon's engram, is the whole of one perspective—not of *any* perspective, but of a perspective in a place where there is nervous tissue, or at any rate living tissue of some sort. Perception also, as we saw, can only be defined in terms of perspectives. Thus the conception of subjectivity, i.e. of the "passive" place of a particular, though not alone sufficient to define mind, is clearly an essential element in the definition.

I have maintained throughout these lectures that the data of psychology do not differ in their intrinsic character from the data of physics. I have maintained that sensations are data for psychology and physics equally, while images, which may be in some sense exclusively psychological data, can only be distinguished from sensations by their correlations, not by what they are in themselves. It is now necessary, however, to examine the notion of a "datum," and to obtain, if possible, a definition of this notion.

The notion of "data" is familiar throughout science, and is usually treated by men of science as though it were perfectly clear. Psychologists, on the other hand, find great difficulty in the conception. "Data" are naturally defined in terms of theory of knowledge: they are those propositions of which the truth is known without demonstration, so that they may be used as premises in proving other propositions. Further, when a proposition which is a datum asserts the existence of something, we say that the something is a datum, as well as the proposition asserting its existence. Thus those objects of whose existence we become certain through perception are said to be data.

There is some difficulty in connecting this epistemological definition of "data" with our psychological analysis of knowledge; but until such a connection has been effected, we have no right to use the conception "data."

It is clear, in the first place, that there can be no datum apart from a belief. A sensation which merely comes and goes is not a datum; it only becomes a datum when it is remembered. Similarly, in perception, we do not have a datum unless we have a *judgment* of perception. In the sense in which objects (as opposed to propositions) are data, it would seem natural to say that those objects of which we are conscious are data. But consciousness, as we have seen, is a complex notion, involving beliefs, as well as mnemic phenomena such as are required for perception and memory. It follows that no datum is theo-

retically indubitable, since no belief is infallible; it follows also
that every datum has a greater or less degree of vagueness, since
there is always some vagueness in memory and the meaning of
images.

Data are not those things of which our consciousness is
earliest in time. At every period of life, after we have become
capable of thought, some of our beliefs are obtained by inference, while others are not. A belief may pass from either
of these classes into the other, and may therefore become, or
cease to be, a belief giving a datum. When, in what follows, I
speak of data, I do not mean the things of which we feel sure
before scientific study begins, but the things which, when a
science is well advanced, appear as affording grounds for other
parts of the science, without themselves being believed on any
ground except observation. I assume, that is to say, a trained
observer, with an analytic attention, knowing the sort of thing
to look for, and the sort of thing that will be important. What
he observes is, at the stage of science which he has reached, a
datum for his science. It is just as sophisticated and elaborate
as the theories which he bases upon it, since only trained habits
and much practice enable a man to make the kind of observation that will be scientifically illuminating. Nevertheless, when
once it has been observed, belief in it is not based on inference
and reasoning, but merely upon its having been seen. In this
way its logical status differs from that of the theories which are
proved by its means.

In any science other than psychology the datum is primarily
a perception, in which only the sensational core is ultimately
and theoretically a datum, though some such accretions as
turn the sensation into a perception are practically unavoidable. But if we postulate an ideal observer, he will be able to
isolate the sensation, and treat this alone as datum. There is,
therefore, an important sense in which we may say that, if we
analyse as much as we ought, our data, outside psychology, consist of sensations, which include within themselves certain
spatial and temporal relations.

Applying this remark to physiology, we see that the nerves

and brain as physical objects are not truly data; they are to be replaced, in the ideal structure of science, by the sensations through which the physiologist is said to perceive them. The passage from these sensations to nerves and brain as physical objects belongs really to the initial stage in the theory of physics, and ought to be placed in the reasoned part, not in the part supposed to be observed. To say we see the nerves is like saying we hear the nightingale; both are convenient but inaccurate expressions. We hear a sound which we believe to be causally connected with the nightingale, and we see a sight which we believe to be causally connected with a nerve. But in each case it is only the sensation that ought, in strictness, to be called a datum. Now, sensations are certainly among the data of psychology. Therefore all the data of the physical sciences are also psychological data. It remains to inquire whether all the data of psychology are also data of physical science, and especially of physiology.

If we have been right in our analysis of mind, the ultimate data of psychology are only sensations and images and their relations. Beliefs, desires, volitions, and so on, appeared to us to be complex phenomena consisting of sensations and images variously interrelated. Thus (apart from certain relations) the occurrences which seem most distinctively mental, and furthest removed from physics, are, like physical objects, constructed or inferred, not part of the original stock of data in the perfected science. From both ends, therefore, the difference between physical and psychological data is diminished. Is there ultimately no difference, or do images remain as irreducibly and exclusively psychological? In view of the causal definition of the difference between images and sensations, this brings us to a new question, namely: Are the causal laws of psychology different from those of any other science, or are they really physiological?

Certain ambiguities must be removed before this question can be adequately discussed.

First, there is the distinction between rough approximate laws and such as appear to be precise and general. I shall return to the former presently; it is the latter that I wish to discuss now.

Matter, as defined at the end of Lecture V, is a logical fiction, invented because it gives a convenient way of stating causal laws. Except in cases of perfect regularity in appearances (of which we can have no experience), the actual appearances of a piece of matter are not members of that ideal system of regular appearances which is defined as being the matter in question. But the matter is, after all, inferred from its appearances, which are used to *verify* physical laws. Thus, in so far as physics is an empirical and verifiable science, it must assume or prove that the inference from appearances to matter is, in general, legitimate, and it must be able to tell us, more or less, what appearances to expect. It is through this question of verifiability and empirical applicability to experience that we are led to a theory of matter such as I advocate. From the consideration of this question it results that physics, in so far as it is an empirical science, not a logical phantasy, is concerned with particulars of just the same sort as those which psychology considers under the name of sensations. The causal laws of physics, so interpreted, differ from those of psychology only by the fact that they connect a particular with other appearances in the same piece of matter, rather than with other appearances in the same perspective. That is to say, they group together particulars having the same "active" place, while psychology groups together those having the same "passive" place. Some particulars, such as images, have no "active" place, and therefore belong exclusively to psychology.

We can now understand the distinction between physics and psychology. The nerves and brain are matter: our visual sensations when we look at them may be, and I think are, members of the system constituting irregular appearances of this matter, but are not the whole of the system. Psychology is concerned, *inter alia,* with our sensations when we see a piece of matter, as opposed to the matter which we see. Assuming, as we must, that our sensations have physical causes, their causal laws are nevertheless radically different from the laws of physics, since the consideration of a single sensation requires the breaking up of the group of which it is a member. When a sensation is used to verify physics, it is used merely as a sign of a certain material phenomenon, i.e. of a group of particulars of which it is a member. But when it is studied by psychology, it is taken away from that group and put into quite a different context, where it causes images or voluntary movements. It is primarily this different grouping that is characteristic of psychology as opposed to all the physical sciences, including physiology; a secondary difference is that images, which belong to psychology, are not easily to be included among the aspects which constitute a physical thing or piece of matter.

There remains, however, an important question, namely: Are mental events causally dependent upon physical events in a sense in which the converse dependence does not hold? Before we can discuss the answer to this question, we must first be clear as to what our question means.

When, given A, it is possible to infer B, but given B, it is not possible to infer A, we say that B is dependent upon A in a sense in which A is not dependent upon B. Stated in logical terms, this amounts to saying that, when we know a many-one relation of A to B, B is dependent upon A in respect of this relation. If the relation is a causal law, we say that B is causally dependent upon A. The illustration that chiefly concerns us is the system of appearances of a physical object. We can, broadly speaking, infer distant appearances from near ones, but not vice versa. All men look alike when they are a mile away, hence when we see a man a mile off we cannot tell what he will look like when he is only a yard away. But when we see him a yard away, we can tell what he will look like a mile away. Thus the nearer view gives us more valuable information, and the distant view is causally dependent upon it in a sense in which it is not causally dependent upon the distant view.

It is this greater causal potency of the near appearance that leads physics to state its causal laws in terms of that system of regular appearances to which the nearest appearances increasingly approximate, and that makes it value information derived from the microscope or telescope. It is clear that our sensations, considered as irregular appearances of physical objects, share the causal dependence belonging to comparatively distant appearances; therefore in our sensational life we are in causal dependence upon physical laws.

This, however, is not the most important or interesting part of our question. It is the causation of images that is the vital problem. We have seen that they are subject to mnemic causation, and that mnemic causation may be reducible to ordinary physical causation in nervous tissue. This is the question upon which our attitude must turn towards what may be called materialism. One sense of materialism is the view that all mental phenomena are causally dependent upon physical phenomena in the above-defined sense of causal dependence. Whether this is the case or not, I do not profess to know. The question seems to me the same as the question whether mnemic causation is ultimate, which we considered without deciding in Lecture IV. But I think the bulk of the evidence points to the materialistic answer as the more probable.

In considering the causal laws of psychology, the distinction between rough generalizations and exact laws is important. There are many rough generalizations in psychology, not only of the sort by which we govern our ordinary behaviour to each other, but also of a more nearly scientific kind. Habit and association belong among such laws. I will give an illustration of the kind of law that can be obtained. Suppose a person has frequently experienced A and B in close temporal contiguity, an association will be established, so that A, or an image of A, tends to cause an image of B. The question arises: will the association work in either direction, or only from the one which has occurred earlier to the one which has occurred later? In an article by Mr. Wohlgemuth, called "The Direction of Associations" (*British Journal of Psychology*, vol. v. part iv, March, 1913), it is claimed to be proved by experiment that, in so far as motor memory (i.e. memory of movements) is concerned, association works only from earlier to later, while in visual and auditory memory this is not the case, but the later of two neighbouring experiences may recall the earlier as well as the earlier the later. It is suggested that motor memory is physiological, while visual and auditory memory are more truly psychological. But that is not the point which concerns us in the illustration. The point which concerns us is that a law of association, established by purely psychological observation, is a purely psychological law, and may serve as a sample of what is possible in the way of discovering such laws. It is, however, still no more than a rough generalization, a statistical average. It cannot tell us what will result from a given cause on a given occasion. It is a law of tendency, not a precise and invariable law such as those of physics aim at being.

If we wish to pass from the law of habit, stated as a tendency or average, to something more precise and invariable, we seem driven to the nervous system. We can more or less guess how an occurrence produces a change in the brain, and how its repetition gradually produces something analogous to the channel of a river, along which currents flow more easily than in neighbouring paths. We can perceive that in this way, if we had more knowledge, the tendency to habit through repetition might be replaced by a precise account of the effect of each occurrence in bringing about a modification of the sort from which habit would ultimately result. It is such considerations that make students of psycho-physiology materialistic in their methods, whatever they may be in their metaphysics. There are, of course, exceptions, such as Professor J. S. Haldane,[1] who maintains that it is theoretically impossible to obtain physiological explanations of psychical phenomena, or physical explanations of physiological phenomena. But I think the bulk of expert opinion, in practice, is on the other side.

The question whether it is possible to obtain precise causal laws in which the causes are psychological, not material, is one of detailed investigation. I have done what I could to make clear the nature of the question, but I do not believe that it is possible as yet to answer it with any confidence. It seems to be by no means an insoluble question, and we may hope that science will be able to produce sufficient grounds for regarding

1 See his book, *The New Psychology and Other Addresses* ([London:] Charles Griffin & Co., 1919).

one answer as much more probable than the other. But for the moment, I do not see how we can come to a decision.

I think, however, on grounds of the theory of matter explained in Lectures V and VII, that an ultimate scientific account of what goes on in the world, if it were ascertainable, would resemble psychology rather than physics in what we found to be the decisive difference between them. I think, that is to say, that such an account would not be content to speak, even formally, as though matter, which is a logical fiction, were the ultimate reality. I think that, if our scientific knowledge were adequate to the task, which it neither is nor is likely to become, it would exhibit the laws of correlation of the particulars constituting a momentary condition of a material unit, and would state the causal laws[1] of the world in terms of these particulars, not in terms of matter. Causal laws so stated would, I believe, be applicable to psychology and physics equally; the science in which they were stated would succeed in achieving what metaphysics has vainly attempted, namely a unified account of what really happens, wholly true even if not the whole of truth, and free from all convenient fictions or unwarrantable assumptions of metaphysical entities. A causal law applicable to particulars would count as a law of physics if it could be stated in terms of those fictitious systems of regular appearances which are matter; if this were not the case, it would count as a law of psychology if one of the particulars were a sensation or an image, i.e. were subject to mnemic causation. I believe that the realization of the complexity of a material unit, and its analysis into constituents analogous to sensations, is of the utmost importance to philosophy, and vital for any understanding of the relations between mind and matter, between our perceptions and the world which they perceive. It is in this direction, I am convinced, that we must look for the solution of many ancient perplexities.

It is probable that the whole science of mental occurrences,

[1] In a perfected science, causal laws will take the form of differential equations—or of finite-difference equations, if the theory of quanta should prove correct.

especially where its initial definitions are concerned, could be simplified by the development of the fundamental unifying science in which the causal laws of particulars are sought, rather than the causal laws of those systems of particulars that constitute the material units of physics. This fundamental science would cause physics to become derivative, in the sort of way in which theories of the constitution of the atom make chemistry derivative from physics; it would also cause psychology to appear less singular and isolated among sciences. If we are right in this, it is a wrong philosophy of matter which has caused many of the difficulties in the philosophy of mind—difficulties which a right philosophy of matter would cause to disappear.

The conclusions at which we have arrived may be summed up as follows:

I. Physics and psychology are not distinguished by their material. Mind and matter alike are logical constructions; the particulars out of which they are constructed, or from which they are inferred, have various relations, some of which are studied by physics, others by psychology. Broadly speaking, physics group particulars by their active places, psychology by their passive places.

II. The two most essential characteristics of the causal laws which would naturally be called psychological are *subjectivity* and *mnemic causation;* these are not unconnected, since the causal unit in mnemic causation is the group of particulars having a given passive place at a given time, and it is by this manner of grouping that subjectivity is defined.

III. Habit, memory and thought are all developments of mnemic causation. It is probable, though not certain, that mnemic causation is derivative from ordinary physical causation in nervous (and other) tissue.

IV. Consciousness is a complex and far from universal characteristic of mental phenomena.

V. Mind is a matter of degree, chiefly exemplified in number and complexity of habits.

VI. All our data, both in physics and psychology, are subject

158 PART FOUR: PSYCHOLOGY

to psychological causal laws; but physical causal laws, at least in
traditional physics, can only be stated in terms of matter, which
is both inferred and constructed, never a datum. In this respect
psychology is nearer to what actually exists.

PART FIVE

PART FIVE

Causation and Inference

'Cause' or 'causal law' is a notion which has an important place in Russell's philosophy of science, and indeed
is of central importance in any philosophy of science. So,
too, we find the discussion of the justification of scientific
inference given a central place. Russell has referred frequently to both these topics in the course of the selections
in this book. Part Five consists of explicit discussions of
causation and scientific inference.

Chapter One is a careful account of the meaning of
'cause,' 'causal law,' 'determinism,' and their role in
science.

Chapter Two is a consideration of the need to assume
certain methodological postulates to justify scientific inference. In his earlier writings, Russell assumed the validity of the principle of induction, using this principle to
justify inferences from known data to unobserved instances
and laws. Later he came to believe that the principle of
induction should be discarded in favor of several more
specific postulates which would justify cases of 'non-demonstrative inference.' For his earlier view, the reader is
referred to *The Problems of Philosophy* (1912), Chapter
Six.

CHAPTER ONE

On the Notion of Cause

In the following paper I wish, first, to maintain that the word "cause" is so inextricably bound up with misleading associations as to make its complete extrusion from the philosophical vocabulary desirable; secondly, to inquire what principle, if any, is employed in science in place of the supposed "law of causality" which philosophers imagine to be employed; thirdly, to exhibit certain confusions, especially in regard to teleology and determinism, which appear to me to be connected with erroneous notions as to causality.

All philosophers, of every school, imagine that causation is one of the fundamental axioms or postulates of science, yet, oddly enough, in advanced sciences such as gravitational astronomy, the word "cause" never occurs. Dr. James Ward, in his *Naturalism and Agnosticism,* makes this a ground of complaint against physics: the business of those who wish to ascertain the ultimate truth about the world, he apparently thinks, should be the discovery of causes, yet physics never even seeks them. To me it seems that philosophy ought not to assume such legislative functions, and that the reason why physics has ceased to look for causes is that, in fact, there are no such things. The law of causality, I believe, like much that passes muster among philosophers, is a relic of a bygone age, surviving, like the monarchy, only because it is erroneously supposed to do no harm.

From *Mysticism and Logic* by Bertrand Russell (1st edn., 1918, 2nd edn., 1929), Chapter IX, pp. 180-208. Reprinted by permission of the publishers, George Allen & Unwin Ltd., London. This selection originally appeared in *Proceedings of the Aristotelian Society,* Vol. XIII (1912-1913).

In order to find out what philosophers commonly understand
by "cause," I consulted Baldwin's *Dictionary,* and was rewarded
beyond my expectations, for I found the following three mutually incompatible definitions:—

> CAUSALITY. (1) The necessary connection of events in the time-
> series. . . .
> CAUSE (notion of). Whatever may be included in the thought
> or perception of a process as taking place in consequence of
> another process. . . .
> CAUSE AND EFFECT. (1) Cause and effect . . . are correlative
> terms denoting any two distinguishable things, phases, or
> aspects of reality, which are so related to each other that
> whenever the first ceases to exist the second comes into exist-
> ence immediately after, and whenever the second comes into
> existence the first has ceased to exist immediately before.

Let us consider these three definitions in turn. The first,
obviously, is unintelligible without a definition of "necessary."
Under this head, Baldwin's *Dictionary* gives the following:—

> NECESSARY. That is necessary which not only is true, but would
> be true under all circumstances. Something more than brute
> compulsion is, therefore, involved in the conception; there is
> a general law under which the thing takes place.

The notion of cause is so intimately connected with that of
necessity that it will be no digression to linger over the above
definition, with a view to discovering, if possible, *some* meaning
of which it is capable; for, as it stands, it is very far from having
any definite signification.

The first point to notice is that, if any meaning is to be given
to the phrase "would be true under all circumstances," the subject of it must be a propositional function, not a proposition.[1] A
proposition is simply true or false, and that ends the matter:
there can be no question of "circumstances." "Charles I's head
was cut off" is just as true in summer as in winter, on Sundays as

---

[1] A propositional function is an expression containing a variable, or undetermined constituent, and becoming a proposition as soon as a definite
value is assigned to the variable. Examples are: "A is A," "*x* is a number."
The variable is called the *argument* of the function.

on Mondays. Thus when it is worth saying that something "would be true under all circumstances," the something in question must be a propositional function, i.e. an expression containing a variable, and becoming a proposition when a value is assigned to the variable; the varying "circumstances" alluded to are then the different values of which the variable is capable. Thus if "necessary" means "what is true under all circumstances," then "if x is a man, x is mortal" is necessary, because it is true for any possible value of x. Thus we should be led to the following definition:—

NECESSARY is a predicate of a propositional function, meaning that it is true for all possible values of its argument or arguments.

Unfortunately, however, the definition in Baldwin's *Dictionary* says that what is necessary is not only "true under all circumstances" but is also "true." Now these two are incompatible. Only propositions can be "true," and only propositional functions can be "true under all circumstances." Hence the definition as it stands is nonsense. What is meant seems to be this: "A proposition is necessary when it is a value of a propositional function which is true under all circumstances, i.e. for all values of its argument or arguments." But if we adopt this definition, the same proposition will be necessary or contingent according as we choose one or other of its terms as the argument to our propositional function. For example, "if Socrates is a man, Socrates is mortal," is necessary if Socrates is chosen as argument, but not if *man* or *mortal* is chosen. Again, "if Socrates is a man, Plato is mortal," will be necessary if either Socrates or *man* is chosen as argument, but not if Plato or *mortal* is chosen. However, this difficulty can be overcome by specifying the constituent which is to be regarded as argument, and we thus arrive at the following definition:—

A proposition is *necessary* with respect to a given constituent if it remains true when that constituent is altered in any way compatible with the proposition remaining significant.

We may now apply this definition to the definition of causality quoted above. It is obvious that the argument must be the time at which the earlier event occurs. Thus an instance of causality will be such as: "If the event e_1 occurs at the time t_1, it will be followed by the event e_2." This proposition is intended to be necessary with respect to t_1, i.e. to remain true however t_1 may be varied. Causality, as a universal law, will then be the following: "Given any event e_1, there is an event e_2 such that, whenever e_1 occurs, e_2 occurs later." But before this can be considered precise, we must specify how much later e_2 is to occur. Thus the principle becomes:—

Given any event e_1, there is an event e_2 and a time-interval τ such that, whenever e_1 occurs, e_2 follows after an interval τ.

I am not concerned as yet to consider whether this law is true or false. For the present, I am merely concerned to discover what the law of causality is supposed to be. I pass, therefore, to the other definitions quoted above.

The second definition need not detain us long, for two reasons. First, because it is psychological: not the "thought or perception" of a process, but the process itself, must be what concerns us in considering causality. Secondly, because it is circular: in speaking of a process as "taking place in consequence of" another process, it introduces the very notion of cause which was to be defined.

The third definition is by far the most precise; indeed as regards clearness it leaves nothing to be desired. But a great difficulty is caused by the temporal contiguity of cause and effect which the definition asserts. No two instants are contiguous, since the time-series is compact; hence either the cause or the effect or both must, if the definition is correct, endure for a finite time; indeed, by the wording of the definition it is plain that both are assumed to endure for a finite time. But then we are faced with a dilemma: if the cause is a process involving change within itself, we shall require (if causality is universal) causal relations between its earlier and later parts; moreover, it would seem that only the later parts can be relevant to the effect,

since the earlier parts are not contiguous to the effect, and therefore (by the definition) cannot influence the effect. Thus we
shall be led to diminish the duration of the cause without limit,
and however much we may diminish it, there will still remain
an earlier part which might be altered without altering the
effect, so that the true cause, as defined, will not have been
reached, for it will be observed that the definition excludes
plurality of causes. If, on the other hand, the cause is purely
static, involving no change within itself, then, in the first place,
no such cause is to be found in nature, and in the second place,
it seems strange—too strange to be accepted, in spite of bare
logical possibility—that the cause, after existing placidly for
some time, should suddenly explode into the effect, when it
might just as well have done so at any earlier time, or have gone
on unchanged without producing its effect. This dilemma,
therefore, is fatal to the view that cause and effect can be contiguous in time; if there are causes and effects, they must be
separated by a finite time-interval τ, as was assumed in the above
interpretation of the first definition.

What is essentially the same statement of the law of causality
as the one elicited above from the first of Baldwin's definitions
is given by other philosophers. Thus John Stuart Mill says:—

> The Law of Causation, the recognition of which is the main
> pillar of inductive science, is but the familiar truth, that in-
> variability of succession is found by observation to obtain
> between every fact in nature and some other fact which has
> preceded it.[1]

And Bergson, who has rightly perceived that the law as stated
by philosophers is worthless, nevertheless continues to suppose
that it is used in science. Thus he says:—

> Now, it is argued, this law [the law of causality] means that
> every phenomenon is determined by its conditions, or, in
> other words, that the same causes produce the same effects.[2]

1 *Logic*, Book III, Chapter V, § 2.
2 *Time and Free Will* [by Henri Bergson, trans F. L. Pogson (London:
George Allen & Co., and New York: Macmillan, 1910)], p. 199.

And again:—

> We perceive physical phenomena, and these phenomena obey laws. This means: (1) That phenomena *a, b, c, d,* previously perceived, can occur again in the same shape; (2) that a certain phenomenon P, which appeared after the conditions *a, b, c, d,* and after these conditions only, will not fail to recur as soon as the same conditions are again present.[1]

A great part of Bergson's attack on science rests on the assumption that it employs this principle. In fact, it employs no such principle, but philosophers—even Bergson—are too apt to take their views on science from each other, not from science. As to what the principle is, there is a fair consensus among philosophers of different schools. There are, however, a number of difficulties which at once arise. I omit the question of plurality of causes for the present, since other graver questions have to be considered. Two of these, which are forced on our attention by the above statement of the law, are the following:—

(1) What is meant by an "event"?
(2) How long may the time-interval be between cause and effect?

(1) An "event," in the statement of the law, is obviously intended to be something that is likely to recur since otherwise the law becomes trivial. It follows that an "event" is not a particular, but some universal of which there may be many instances. It follows also that an "event" must be something short of the whole state of the universe, since it is highly improbable that this will recur. What is meant by an "event" is something like striking a match, or dropping a penny into the slot of an automatic machine. If such an event is to recur, it must not be defined too narrowly: we must not state with what degree of force the match is to be struck, nor what is to be the temperature of the penny. For if such considerations were relevant, our "event" would occur at most once, and the law would cease to give information. An "event," then, is a universal defined sufficiently

1 *Time and Free Will*, p. 202.

widely to admit of many particular occurrences in time being instances of it.

(2) The next question concerns the time-interval. Philosophers, no doubt, think of cause and effect as contiguous in time, but this, for reasons already given, is impossible. Hence, since there are no infinitesimal time-intervals, there must be some finite lapse of time τ between cause and effect. This, however, at once raises insuperable difficulties. However short we make the interval τ, something may happen during this interval which prevents the expected result. I put my penny in the slot, but before I can draw out my ticket there is an earthquake which upsets the machine and my calculations. In order to be sure of the expected effect, we must know that there is nothing in the environment to interfere with it. But this means that the supposed cause is not, by itself, adequate to insure the effect. And as soon as we include the environment, the probability of repetition is diminished, until at last, when the whole environment is included, the probability of repetition becomes almost *nil*.

In spite of these difficulties, it must, of course, be admitted that many fairly dependable regularities of sequence occur in daily life. It is these regularities that have suggested the supposed law of causality; where they are found to fail, it is thought that a better formulation could have been found which would have never failed. I am far from denying that there may be such sequences which in fact never do fail. It may be that there will never be an exception to the rule that when a stone of more than a certain mass, moving with more than a certain velocity, comes in contact with a pane of glass of less than a certain thickness, the glass breaks. I also do not deny that the observation of such regularities, even when they are not without exceptions, is useful in the infancy of a science: the observation that unsupported bodies in air usually fall was a stage on the way to the law of gravitation. What I deny is that science assumes the existence of invariable uniformities of sequence of this kind, or that it aims at discovering them. All such uniformities, as we saw, depend upon a certain vagueness in the definition of the "events." That bodies fall is a vague qualitative statement;

science wishes to know how fast they fall. This depends upon the shape of the bodies and the density of the air. It is true that there is more nearly uniformity when they fall in a vacuum; so far as Galileo could observe, the uniformity is then complete. But later it appeared that even there the latitude made a difference, and the altitude. Theoretically, the position of the sun and moon must make a difference. In short, every advance in a science takes us farther away from the crude uniformities which are first observed, into greater differentiation of antecedent and consequent, and into a continually wider circle of antecedents recognised as relevant.

The principle "same cause, same effect," which philosophers imagine to be vital to science, is therefore utterly otiose. As soon as the antecedents have been given sufficiently fully to enable the consequent to be calculated with some exactitude, the antecedents have become so complicated that it is very unlikely they will ever recur. Hence, if this were the principle involved, science would remain utterly sterile.

The importance of these considerations lies partly in the fact that they lead to a more correct account of scientific procedure, partly in the fact that they remove the analogy with human volition which makes the conception of cause such a fruitful source of fallacies. The latter point will become clearer by the help of some illustrations. For this purpose I shall consider a few maxims which have played a great part in the history of philosophy.

(1) "Cause and effect must more or less resemble each other." This principle was prominent in the philosophy of occasionalism, and is still by no means extinct. It is still often thought, for example, that mind could not have grown up in a universe which previously contained nothing mental, and one ground for this belief is that matter is too dissimilar from mind to have been able to cause it. Or, more particularly, what are termed the nobler parts of our nature are supposed to be inexplicable, unless the universe always contained something at least equally noble which could cause them. All such views seem to depend upon assuming some unduly simplified law of causality; for, in any legitimate sense of "cause" and "effect," science seems to

show that they are usually very widely dissimilar, the "cause" being, in fact, two states of the whole universe, and the "effect" some particular event.

(2) "Cause is analogous to volition, since there must be an intelligible *nexus* between cause and effect." This maxim is, I think, often unconsciously in the imaginations of philosophers who would reject it when explicitly stated. It is probably operative in the view we have just been considering, that mind could not have resulted from a purely material world. I do not profess to know what is meant by "intelligible"; it seems to mean "familiar to imagination." Nothing is less "intelligible," in any other sense, than the connection between an act of will and its fulfilment. But obviously the sort of nexus desired between cause and effect is such as could only hold between the "events" which the supposed law of causality contemplates; the laws which replace causality in such a science as physics leave no room for any two events between which a nexus could be sought.

(3) "The cause *compels* the effect in some sense in which the effect does not compel the cause." This belief seems largely operative in the dislike of determinism; but, as a matter of fact, it is connected with our second maxim, and falls as soon as that is abandoned. We may define "compulsion" as follows: "Any set of circumstances is said to compel A when A desires to do something which the circumstances prevent, or to abstain from something which the circumstances cause." This presupposes that some meaning has been found for the word "cause"—a point to which I shall return later. What I want to make clear at present is that compulsion is a very complex notion, involving thwarted desire. So long as a person does what he wishes to do, there is no compulsion, however much his wishes may be calculable by the help of earlier events. And where desire does not come in, there can be no question of compulsion. Hence it is, in general, misleading to regard the cause as compelling the effect.

A vaguer form of the same maxim substitutes the word "determine" for the word "compel"; we are told that the cause *determines* the effect in a sense in which the effect does not *determine* the cause. It is not quite clear what is meant by "determining"; the only precise sense, so far as I know, is that of a function or one-many relation. If we admit plurality of causes, but not of effects, that is, if we suppose that, given the cause, the effect must be such-and-such, but, given the effect, the cause may have been one of many alternatives, then we may say that the cause determines the effect, but not the effect the cause. Plurality of causes, however, results only from conceiving the effect vaguely and narrowly and the cause precisely and widely. Many antecedents may "cause" a man's death, because his death is vague and narrow. But if we adopt the opposite course, taking as the "cause" the drinking of a dose of arsenic, and as the "effect" the whole state of the world five minutes later, we shall have plurality of effects instead of plurality of causes. Thus the supposed lack of symmetry between "cause" and "effect" is illusory.

(4) "A cause cannot operate when it has ceased to exist, because what has ceased to exist is nothing." This is a common maxim, and a still more common unexpressed prejudice. It has, I fancy, a good deal to do with the attractiveness of Bergson's "*durée*": since the past has effects now, it must still exist in some sense. The mistake in this maxim consists in the supposition that causes "operate" at all. A volition "operates" when what it wills takes place; but nothing can operate except a volition. The belief that causes "operate" results from assimilating them, consciously or unconsciously, to volitions. We have already seen that, if there are causes at all, they must be separated by a finite interval of time from their effects, and thus cause their effects after they have ceased to exist.

It may be objected to the above definition of a volition "operating" that it only operates when it "causes" what it wills, not when it merely happens to be followed by what it wills. This certainly represents the usual view of what is meant by a violation "operating," but as it involves the very view of causation which we are engaged in combating, it is not open to us as a definition. We may say that a volition "operates" when there is some law in virtue of which a similar volition in rather similar circumstances will usually be followed by what it wills. But this is a vague conception, and introduces ideas which we have not yet considered. What is chiefly important to notice is that the usual notion of "operating" is not open to us if we reject, as I contend that we should, the usual notion of causation.

(5) "A cause cannot operate except where it is." This maxim is very widespread; it was urged against Newton, and has remained a source of prejudice against "action at a distance." In philosophy it has led to a denial of transient action, and thence to monism or Leibnizian monadism. Like the analogous maxim concerning temporal contiguity, it rests upon the assumption that causes "operate," i.e. that they are in some obscure way analogous to volitions. And, as in the case of temporal contiguity, the inferences drawn from this maxim are wholly groundless.

I return now to the question, What law or laws can be found to take the place of the supposed law of causality?

First, without passing beyond such uniformities of sequence as are contemplated by the traditional law, we may admit that, if any such sequence has been observed in a great many cases, and has never been found to fail, there is an inductive probability that it will be found to hold in future cases. If stones have hitherto been found to break windows, it is probable that they will continue to do so. This, of course, assumes the inductive principle, of which the truth may reasonably be questioned; but as this principle is not our present concern, I shall in this discussion treat it as indubitable. We may then say, in the case of any such frequently observed sequence, that the earlier event is the *cause* and the later event the *effect*.

Several considerations, however, make such special sequences very different from the traditional relation of cause and effect. In the first place, the sequence, in any hitherto unobserved instance, is no more than probable, whereas the relation of cause and effect was supposed to be necessary. I do not mean by this merely that we are not sure of having discovered a true case of cause and effect; I mean that, even when we have a case of cause and effect in our present sense, all that is meant is that on grounds of observation, it is probable that when one occurs the other will also occur. Thus in our present sense, A may be the cause of B even if there actually are cases where B does not follow A. Striking a match will be the cause of its igniting, in spite of the fact that some matches are damp and fail to ignite.

In the second place, it will not be assumed that *every* event has some antecedent which is its cause in this sense; we shall only believe in causal sequences where we find them, without any presumption that they always are to be found.

In the third place, *any* case of sufficiently frequent sequence will be causal in our present sense; for example, we shall not refuse to say that night is the cause of day. Our repugnance to saying this arises from the ease with which we can imagine the sequence to fail, but owing to the fact that cause and effect must be separated by a finite interval of time, *any* such sequence *might* fail through the interposition of other circumstances in the interval. Mill, discussing this instance of night and day, says:—

> It is necessary to our using the word cause, that we should believe not only that the antecedent always *has* been followed by the consequent, but that as long as the present constitution of things endures, it always *will* be so.[1]

In this sense, we shall have to give up the hope of finding causal laws such as Mill contemplated; any causal sequence which we have observed may at any moment be falsified without a falsification of any laws of the kind that the more advanced sciences aim at establishing.

In the fourth place, such laws of probable sequence, though useful in daily life and in the infancy of a science, tend to be displaced by quite different laws as soon as a science is successful. The law of gravitation will illustrate what occurs in any advanced science. In the motions of mutually gravitating bodies, there is nothing that can be called a cause, and nothing that can be called an effect; there is merely a formula. Certain differential equations can be found, which hold at every instant for every

[1] *Loc. cit.*, § 6.

particle of the system, and which, given the configuration and velocities at one instant, or the configurations at two instants, render the configuration at any other earlier or later instant theoretically calculable. That is to say, the configuration at any instant is a function of that instant and the configurations at two given instants. This statement holds throughout physics, and not only in the special case of gravitation. But there is nothing that could be properly called "cause" and nothing that could be properly called "effect" in such a system.

No doubt the reason why the old "law of causality" has so long continued to pervade the books of philosophers is simply that the idea of a function is unfamiliar to most of them, and therefore they seek an unduly simplified statement. There is no question of repetitions of the "same" cause producing the "same" effect; it is not in any sameness of causes and effects that the constancy of scientific law consists, but in sameness of relations. And even "sameness of relations" is too simple a phrase; "sameness of differential equations" is the only correct phrase. It is impossible to state this accurately in non-mathematical language; the nearest approach would be as follows: "There is a constant relation between the state of the universe at any instant and the rate of change in the rate at which any part of the universe is changing at that instant, and this relation is many-one, i.e. such that the rate of change in the rate of change is determinate when the state of the universe is given." If the "law of causality" is to be something actually discoverable in the practice of science, the above proposition has a better right to the name than any "law of causality" to be found in the books of philosophers.

In regard to the above principle, several observations must be made:—

(1) No one can pretend that the above principle is *a priori* or self-evident or a "necessity of thought." Nor is it, in any sense, a premiss of science: it is an empirical generalisation from a number of laws which are themselves empirical generalisations.

(2) The law makes no difference between past and future:

the future "determines" the past in exactly the same sense in which the past "determines" the future. The word "determine," here, has a purely logical significance: a certain number of variables "determine" another variable if that other variable is a function of them.

(3) The law will not be empirically verifiable unless the course of events within some sufficiently small volume will be approximately the same in any two states of the universe which only differ in regard to what is at a considerable distance from the small volume in question. For example, motions of planets in the solar system must be approximately the same however the fixed stars may be distributed, provided that all the fixed stars are very much farther from the sun than the planets are. If gravitation varied directly as the distance, so that the most remote stars made the most difference to the motions of the planets, the world might be just as regular and just as much subject to mathematical laws as it is at present, but we could never discover the fact.

(4) Although the old "law of causality" is not assumed by science, something which we may call the "uniformity of nature" is assumed, or rather is accepted on inductive grounds. The uniformity of nature does not assert the trivial principle "same cause, same effect," but the principle of the permanence of laws. That is to say, when a law exhibiting, e.g. an acceleration as a function of the configuration has been found to hold throughout the observable past, it is expected that it will continue to hold in the future, or that, if it does not itself hold, there is some other law, agreeing with the supposed law as regards the past, which will hold for the future. The ground of this principle is simply the inductive ground that it has been found to be true in very many instances; hence the principle cannot be considered certain, but only probable to a degree which cannot be accurately estimated.

The uniformity of nature, in the above sense, although it is assumed in the practice of science, must not, in its generality, be regarded as a kind of major premiss, without which all scientific reasoning would be in error. The assumption that *all* laws of nature are permanent has, of course, less probability

than the assumption that this or that particular law is permanent; and the assumption that a particular law is permanent
for all time has less probability than the assumption that it will
be valid up to such and such a date. Science, in any given case,
will assume what the case requires, but no more. In constructing the *Nautical Almanac* for 1915 it will assume that the law
of gravitation will remain true up to the end of that year; but
it will make no assumption as to 1916 until it comes to the next
volume of the almanac. This procedure is, of course, dictated
by the fact that the uniformity of nature is not known *a priori*,
but is an empirical generalisation, like "all men are mortal."
In all such cases, it is better to argue immediately from the
given particular instances to the new instance, than to argue
by way of a major premiss; the conclusion is only probable in
either case, but acquires a higher probability by the former
method than by the latter.

In all science we have to distinguish two sorts of laws: first,
those that are empirically verifiable but probably only approximate; secondly, those that are not verifiable, but may be exact.
The law of gravitation, for example, in its applications to the
solar system, is only empirically verifiable when it is assumed
that matter outside the solar system may be ignored for such
purposes; we believe this to be only approximately true, but
we cannot empirically verify the law of universal gravitation
which we believe to be exact. This point is very important in
connection with what we may call "relatively isolated systems."
These may be defined as follows:—

> A system relatively isolated during a given period is one
> which, within some assignable margin of error, will behave
> in the same way throughout that period, however the rest
> of the universe may be constituted.
> A system may be called "practically isolated" during a
> given period if, although there *might* be states of the rest
> of the universe which would produce more than the as-
> signed margin of error, there is reason to believe that such
> states do not in fact occur.

Strictly speaking, we ought to specify the respect in which the
system is relatively isolated. For example, the earth is relatively

isolated as regards falling bodies, but not as regards tides; it is *practically* isolated as regards economic phenomena, although, if Jevons' sun-spot theory of commercial crises had been true, it would not have been even practically isolated in this respect.

It will be observed that we cannot prove in advance that a system is isolated. This will be inferred from the observed fact that approximate uniformities can be stated for this system alone. If the complete laws for the whole universe were known, the isolation of a system could be deduced from them; assuming, for example, the law of universal gravitation, the practical isolation of the solar system in this respect can be deduced by the help of the fact that there is very little matter in its neighbourhood. But it should be observed that isolated systems are only important as providing a possibility of *discovering* scientific laws; they have no theoretical importance in the finished structure of a science.

The case where one event A is said to "cause" another event B, which philosophers take as fundamental, is really only the most simplified instance of a practically isolated system. It may happen that, as a result of general scientific laws, whenever A occurs throughout a certain period, it is followed by B; in that case, A and B form a system which is practically isolated throughout that period. It is, however, to be regarded as a piece of good fortune if this occurs; it will always be due to special circumstances, and would not have been true if the rest of the universe had been different though subject to the same laws.

The essential function which causality has been supposed to perform is the possibility of inferring the future from the past, or, more generally, events at any time from events at certain assigned times. Any system in which such inference is possible may be called a "deterministic" system. We may define a deterministic system as follows:—

A system is said to be "deterministic" when, given certain data, $e_1, e_2, \ldots, e_n$, at times $t_1, t_2, \ldots, t_n$ respectively, concerning this system, if E_t is the state of the system at any time t, there is a functional relation of the form

$$E_t = f(e_1, t_1, e_2, t_2, \ldots, e_n, t_n, t). \qquad (A)$$

The system will be "deterministic throughout a given period" if t, in the above formula, may be any time within that period, though outside that period the formula may be no longer true. If the universe, as a whole, is such a system, determinism is true of the universe; if not, not. A system which is part of a deterministic system I shall call "determined"; one which is not part of any such system I shall call "capricious."

The events $e_1, e_2, \ldots, e_n$ I shall call "determinants" of the system. It is to be observed that a system which has one set of determinants will in general have many. In the case of the motions of the planets, for example, the configurations of the solar system at any two given times will be determinants.

We may take another illustration from the hypothesis of psycho-physical parallelism. Let us assume, for the purposes of this illustration, that to a given state of brain a given state of mind always corresponds, and vice versa, i.e. that there is a one-one relation between them, so that each is a function of the other. We may also assume, what is practically certain, that to a given state of a certain brain a given state of the whole material universe corresponds, since it is highly improbable that a given brain is ever twice in exactly the same state. Hence there will be a one-one relation between the state of a given person's mind and the state of the whole material universe. It follows that, if n states of the material universe are determinants of the material universe, then n states of a given man's mind are determinants of the whole material and mental universe—assuming, that is to say, that psycho-physical parallelism is true.

The above illustration is important in connection with a certain confusion which seems to have beset those who have philosophised on the relation of mind and matter. It is often thought that, if the state of the mind is determinate when the state of the brain is given, and if the material world forms a deterministic system, then mind is "subject" to matter in some sense in which matter is not "subject" to mind. But if the state of the brain is also determinate when the state of the mind is given, it must be exactly as true to regard matter as subject to mind as it would be to regard mind as subject to matter. We could, theoretically, work out the history of mind without ever mentioning matter, and then, at the end, deduce that matter must meanwhile have gone through the corresponding history. It is true that if the relation of brain to mind were many-one, not one-one, there would be a one-sided dependence of mind on brain, while conversely, if the relation were one-many, as Bergson supposes, there would be a one-sided dependence of brain on mind. But the dependence involved is, in any case, only logical; it does not mean that we shall be compelled to do things we desire not to do, which is what people instinctively imagine it to mean.

As another illustration we may take the case of mechanism and teleology. A system may be defined as "mechanical" when it has a set of determinants that are purely material, such as the positions of certain pieces of matter at certain times. It is an open question whether the world of mind and matter, as we know it, is a mechanical system or not; let us suppose, for the sake of argument, that it is a mechanical system. This supposition—so I contend—throws no light whatever on the question whether the universe is or is not a "teleological" system. It is difficult to define accurately what is meant by a "teleological" system, but the argument is not much affected by the particular definition we adopt. Broadly, a teleological system is one in which purposes are realised, i.e. in which certain desires—those that are deeper or nobler or more fundamental or more universal or what not—are followed by their realisation. Now the fact—if it be a fact—that the universe is mechanical has no bearing whatever on the question whether it is teleological in the above sense. There might be a mechanical system in which all wishes were realised, and there might be one in which all wishes were thwarted. The question whether, or how far, our actual world is teleological, cannot, therefore, be settled by proving that it is mechanical, and the desire that it should be teleological is no ground for wishing it to be not mechanical.

There is, in all these questions, a very great difficulty in avoiding confusion between what we can infer and what is in fact determined. Let us consider, for a moment, the various senses in which the future may be "determined." There is one sense—and a very important one—in which it is determined quite independently of scientific laws, namely, the sense that it will be what it will be. We all regard the past as determined simply by the fact that it has happened; but for the accident that memory works backward and not forward, we should regard the future as equally determined by the fact that it will happen. "But," we are told, "you cannot alter the past, while you can to some extent alter the future." This view seems to me to rest upon just those errors in regard to causation which it has been my object to remove. You cannot make the past other than it was—true, but this is a mere application of the law of contradiction. If you already know what the past was, obviously it is useless to wish it different. But also you cannot make the future other than it will be; this again is an application of the law of contradiction. And if you happen to know the future—e.g. in the case of a forthcoming eclipse—it is just as useless to wish it different as to wish the past different. "But," it will be rejoined, "our wishes can *cause* the future, sometimes, to be different from what it would be if they did not exist, and they can have no such effect upon the past." This, again, is a mere tautology. An effect being *defined* as something subsequent to its cause, obviously we can have no *effect* upon the past. But that does not mean that the past would not have been different if our present wishes had been different. Obviously, our present wishes are conditioned by the past, and therefore could not have been different unless the past had been different; therefore, if our present wishes were different, the past would be different. Of course, the past cannot be different from what it was, but no more can our present wishes be different from what they are; this again is merely the law of contradiction. The facts seem to be merely (1) that wishing generally depends upon ignorance, and is therefore commoner in regard to the future than in regard to the past; (2) that where a wish concerns the future, it and its realisation very often form a "practically independent system," i.e. many wishes regarding the future are realised. But there seems no doubt that the main difference in our feelings arises from the accidental fact that the past but not the future can be known by memory.

Although the sense of "determined" in which the future is determined by the mere fact that it will be what it will be is sufficient (at least so it seems to me) to refute some opponents of determinism, notably M. Bergson and the pragmatists, yet it is not what most people have in mind when they speak of the future as determined. What they have in mind is a formula by means of which the future can be exhibited, and at least theoretically calculated, as a function of the past. But at this point we meet with a great difficulty, which besets what has been said above about deterministic systems, as well as what is said by others.

If formulæ of any degree of complexity, however great, are admitted, it would seem that any system, whose state at a given moment is a function of certain measurable quantities, *must* be a deterministic system. Let us consider, in illustration, a single material particle, whose co-ordinates at time t are x_t, y_t, z_t. Then, however, the particle moves, there must be, theoretically, functions f_1, f_2, f_3, such that

$$x_t = f_1(t), \qquad y_t = f_2(t), \qquad z_t = f_3(t).$$

It follows that, theoretically, the whole state of the material universe at time t must be capable of being exhibited as a funtion of t. Hence our universe will be deterministic in the sense defined above. But if this be true, no information is conveyed about the universe in stating that it is deterministic. It is true that the formulæ involved may be of strictly infinite complexity, and therefore not practically capable of being written down or apprehended. But except from the point of view of our knowledge, this might seem to be a detail: in itself, if the above considerations are sound, the material universe *must* be deterministic, *must* be subject to laws.

This, however, is plainly not what was intended. The difference between this view and the view intended may be seen as follows. Given some formula which fits the facts hitherto—say the law of gravitation—there will be an infinite number of other formulæ, not empirically distinguishable from it in the past, but diverging from it more and more in the future. Hence, even assuming that there are persistent laws, we shall have no reason for assuming that the law of the inverse square will hold in the future; it may be some other hitherto indistinguishable law that will hold. We cannot say that *every* law which has held hitherto must hold in the future, because past facts which obey one law will also obey others, hitherto indistinguishable but diverging in future. Hence there must, at every moment, be laws hitherto unbroken which are now broken for the first time. What science does, in fact, is to select the *simplest* formula that will fit the facts. But this, quite obviously, is merely a methodological precept, not a law of Nature. If the simplest formula ceases, after a time, to be applicable, the simplest formula that remains applicable is selected, and science has no sense that an axiom has been falsified. We are thus left with the brute fact that, in many departments of science, quite simple laws have hitherto been found to hold. This fact cannot be regarded as having any *a priori* ground, nor can it be used to support inductively the opinion that the same laws will continue; for at every moment laws hitherto true are being falsified, though in the advanced sciences these laws are less simple than those that have remained true. Moreover it would be fallacious to argue inductively from the state of the advanced sciences to the future state of the others, for it may well be that the advanced sciences are advanced simply because, hitherto, their subject-matter has obeyed simple and easily ascertainable laws, while the subject-matter of other sciences has not done so.

The difficulty we have been considering seems to be met partly, if not wholly, by the principle that the *time* must not enter explicitly into our formulæ. All mechanical laws exhibit acceleration as a function of configuration, not of configuration and time jointly; and this principle of the irrelevance of the time may be extended to all scientific laws. In fact we might interpret the "uniformity of nature" as meaning just this, that no scientific law involves the time as an argument, unless, of course, it is given in an integrated form, in which case *lapse* of time, though not absolute time, may appear in our formulæ. Whether this consideration suffices to overcome our difficulty completely, I do not know; but in any case it does much to diminish it.

It will serve to illustrate what has been said if we apply it to the question of free will.

(1) Determinism in regard to the will is the doctrine that our volitions belong to some deterministic system, i.e. are "determined" in the sense defined above. Whether this doctrine is true or false, is a mere question of fact; no *a priori* considerations (if our previous discussions have been correct) can exist on either side. On the one hand, there is no *a priori* category of causality, but merely certain observed uniformities. As a matter of fact, there are observed uniformities in regard to volitions; thus there is some empirical evidence that volitions are determined. But it would be very rash to maintain that the evidence is overwhelming, and it is quite possible that some volitions, as well as some other things, are not determined, except in the sense in which we found that everything must be determined.

(2) But, on the other hand, the subjective sense of freedom, sometimes alleged against determinism, has no bearing on the question whatever. The view that it has a bearing rests upon the belief that causes compel their effects, or that nature enforces obedience to its laws as governments do. These are mere anthropomorphic superstitions, due to assimilation of causes with volitions and of natural laws with human edicts. We feel that our will is not compelled, but that only means that it is not other than we choose it to be. It is one of the demerits of the traditional theory of causality that it has created an artificial opposition between determinism and the freedom of which we are introspectively conscious.

(3) Besides the general question whether volitions are determined, there is the further question whether they are *mechanically* determined, i.e. whether they are part of what was above defined as a mechanical system. This is the question whether they form part of a system with purely material determinants, i.e. whether there are laws which, given certain material data,

make all volitions functions of those data. Here again, there is empirical evidence up to a point, but it is not conclusive in regard to all volitions. It is important to observe, however, that even if volitions are part of a mechanical system, this by no means implies any supremacy of matter over mind. It may well be that the same system which is susceptible of material determinants is also susceptible of mental determinants; thus a mechanical system may be determined by sets of volitions, as well as by sets of material facts. It would seem, therefore, that the reasons which make people dislike the view that volitions are mechanically determined are fallacious.

(4) The notion of *necessity*, which is often associated with determinism, is a confused notion not legitimately deducible from determinism. Three meanings are commonly confounded when necessity is spoken of:—

(α) An *action* is necessary when it will be performed however much the agent may wish to do otherwise. Determinism does not imply that actions are necessary in this sense.

(β) A *propositional function* is necessary when all its values are true. This sense is not relevant to our present discussion.

(γ) A *proposition* is necessary with respect to a given constituent when it is the value, with that constituent as argument, of a necessary propositional function, in other words, when it remains true however that constituent may be varied. In this sense, in a deterministic system, the connection of a volition with its determinants is necessary, if the time at which the determinants occur be taken as the constituent to be varied, the time-interval between the determinants and the volition being kept constant. But this sense of necessity is purely logical, and has no emotional importance.

We may now sum up our discussion of causality. We found first that the law of causality, as usually stated by philosophers, is false, and is not employed in science. We then considered the nature of scientific laws, and found that, instead of stating that one event A is always followed by another event B, they stated functional relations between certain events at certain times, which we called determinants, and other events at earlier or later times or at the same time. We were unable to find any *a priori* category involved: the existence of scientific laws appeared as a purely empirical fact, not necessarily universal, except in a trivial and scientifically useless form. We found that a system with one set of determinants may very likely have other sets of a quite different kind, that, for example, a mechanically determined system may also be teleologically or volitionally determined. Finally we considered the problem of free will: here we found that the reasons for supposing volitions to be determined are strong but not conclusive, and we decided that even if volitions are mechanically determined, that is no reason for denying freedom in the sense revealed by introspection, or for supposing that mechanical events are not determined by volitions. The problem of free will *versus* determinism is therefore, if we were right, mainly illusory, but in part not yet capable of being decisively solved.

CHAPTER TWO

Non-demonstrative Inference

I returned to England in June 1944, after three weeks on the Atlantic. Trinity had awarded me a five-years lectureship and I chose as the subject of my annual course, "Non-Demonstrative Inference," or N-D.I. for short. I had become increasingly aware of the very limited scope of deductive inference as practised in logic and pure mathematics. I realized that all the inferences used both in common sense and in science are of a different sort from those in deductive logic, and are such that, when the premisses are true and the reasoning correct, the conclusion is only probable. During the first six months after my return from America I had rooms in College and enjoyed a feeling of peacefulness in spite of V1's and V2's. I set to work to investigate probability and the kind of inference which confers probability. I found the subject at first somewhat bewildering as there was a tangle of different problems and each thread had to be separated from every other. The positive outcome appeared in *Human Knowledge,* but I did not, in that book, mention the various perplexities and tentative hypotheses through which I had arrived at my final conclusions. I now think this was a mistake, as it made the conclusions appear more slap-dash and less solid than, in fact, they were.

I found the subject of non-demonstrative inference much

larger and much more interesting than I had expected. I found that it had in most discussions been unduly confined to the investigation of induction. I came to the conclusion that inductive arguments, unless they are confined within the limits of common sense, will lead to false conclusions much more often than to true ones. The limitations imposed by common sense are easy to feel but very difficult to formulate. In the end, I came to the conclusion that, although scientific inference needs indemonstrable extra-logical principles, induction is not one of them. It has a part to play, but not as a premiss. I shall return to this subject presently.

Another conclusion which was forced upon me was that not only science, but a great deal that no one sincerely doubts to be knowledge, is impossible if we only know what can be experienced and verified. I felt that much too much emphasis had been laid upon experience, and that, therefore, empiricism as a philosophy must be subjected to important limitations.

I was at first bewildered by the vastness and multiplicity of the problems involved. Seeing that it is of the essence of non-demonstrative inference to confer only probability upon its conclusions, I thought it prudent to begin with an investigation of probability, especially as, on this subject, there existed a body of positive knowledge floating like a raft upon the great ocean of uncertainty. For some months, I studied the calculus of probability and its applications. There are two kinds of probability, of which one is exemplified by statistics, and the other by doubtfulness. Some theorists have thought that they could do with only one of these, and some have thought that they could do with only the other. The mathematical calculus, as usually interpreted, is concerned with the statistical kind of probability. There are fifty-two cards in a pack, and therefore, if you draw a card at random, the chance that it will be the seven of diamonds is one in fifty-two. It is generally assumed, without conclusive evidence, that, if you drew cards at random a great many times, the seven of diamonds would appear about once in every fifty-two times. The subject of probability owed its origin to the interest of aristocrats in games of chance. They hired mathematicians to work out systems which should make gambling lucrative rather than expensive. The mathematicians produced a lot of interesting work, but it does not appear to have enriched their employers.

The theory which considers that all probability is of this statistical kind is called the "frequency" theory. What, for example, is the probability that a person chosen at random from the population of England will be called "Smith"? You find out how many people there are in England and how many of them are called "Smith." You then *define* the probability that a person chosen at random will be called "Smith" as the ratio of the number of Smiths to the number of the total population. This is a perfectly precise mathematical conception, having nothing whatever to do with uncertainty. Uncertainty only comes in when you *apply* the conception as, for example, if you see a stranger across the street and you bet a hundred to one that he is not called "Smith." But so long as you do not apply the calculus of probability to empirical material, it is a perfectly straightforward branch of mathematics with all the exactness and certainty characteristic of mathematics.

There is, however, another, quite different, theory which was adopted by Keynes in his *Treatise on Probability*. He held that there can be a relation between two propositions consisting in the fact that one of them makes the other probable in a greater or less degree. He held that this relation is indefinable and capable of varying degrees, the extreme degrees being when the one proposition makes the truth of the other certain, and when it makes its falsehood certain. He did not believe that all probabilities are numerically measurable or reducible, even in theory, to frequencies.

I came to the conclusion that, wherever probability is definite, the frequency theory is applicable, but that there is another conception, misleadingly called by the same name, to which something more like Keynes's theory is applicable. This other conception I called "degree of credibility" or "degree of doubtfulness." It is obvious that we are much more certain about some things than we are about others, and that our uncertainty often has no statistical aspect. It is true that the statistical aspect can sometimes be discovered where it is not obvious at first sight. I read a book about the Saxon invasion of England which led me to think that Hengist was indubitable but Horsa was perhaps a legend. It would perhaps be possible to put the evidence for Horsa alongside of evidence for other historical characters, and discover in what proportion of cases such evidence had been found to lead aright or to lead astray. But, although this sort of thing is sometimes possible, it certainly does not cover the ground, and leaves degrees of doubtfulness as a necessary conception in the investigation of what passes for knowledge.

It seemed to me that, in the problems with which I was concerned, doubtfulness was much more important than mathematical probability. It was not only that, in the inferences with which I was concerned, the premisses, even if true, do not make the conclusion certain. What was much more important was that the premisses themselves are uncertain. This led me to the conclusion that the mathematical aspects of probability have less to do than might be thought with the problems of scientific inference.

I next devoted myself to a collection of instances where we make inferences that we feel to be quite solid although the inferences in question can only be validated by extra-logical principles. In collecting such instances, I accepted whatever would only be doubted by a philosopher in defence of a theory. Broadly speaking, I did not reject common sense, except where there was some very cogent scientific argument against it. Take a very simple example: suppose you are walking out-of-doors on a sunny day; your shadow walks with you; if you wave your arms, your shadow waves its arms; if you jump, your shadow jumps; for such reasons, you unhesitatingly call it *your* shadow and you have no doubt whatever that it has a causal connection with your body. But, although the inference is one which no sane man would question, it is not logically demonstrative. It is not logically impossible that there should be a dark patch going through movements not unlike the movements of your body, but having an independent existence of its own. I attempted, by collecting as many instances as I could think of in which non-demonstrative inferences seem to us unquestionable, to discover by analysis what extra-logical principles must be true if we are not mistaken in such cases. The evidence in favour of the principles is derived from the instances and not vice versa. There seemed to me to be several such principles, but I came to the conclusion that induction is not one of them.

I found that, for lack of analysis, people had admitted blocks of non-demonstrative inference because they had a subjective prejudice in favour of certain kinds of knowledge, and had rejected other blocks on account of a contrary prejudice. It appeared to me that, in any particular case of an inference which seemed unquestionable, one should discover the principle upon which it depended and accept other inferences depending upon the same principle. I found that almost all philosophers had been mistaken as to what can and what cannot be inferred from experience alone. I divided the problem of empirical knowledge into three stages: (1) knowledge about myself; (2) knowledge about other minds—which includes the acceptance of testimony; and (3) knowledge about the physical world. Beginning with knowledge about myself, I found that solipsism as commonly expounded admits a great deal that is incompatible with the caution by which such a system is inspired. I do not remember anything that happened to me before I was two years old, but I do not think it plausible to maintain that I began to exist at the age of two. And in later life, I am quite convinced that many things happened to me which I do not remember. Even what I remember may have never happened. I have sometimes had dreams in which there were dream-memories that were wholly imaginary. I once dreamt that I was in terror of the police because I "remembered" that, a month ago, Whitehead and I together had murdered Lloyd George. It follows that my recollecting something is not, *per se,* conclusive evidence that the something really happened. The solipsist, therefore, if he is to attain the logical safety of which he is in search, will be

confined to what I call "solipsism of the moment." He will say
not only "I do not know whether the physical world exists or
whether there are minds other than my own," but he will have
to go further and say, "I do not know whether I had a past or
shall have a future, for these things are just as doubtful as the
existence of other people or of the physical world." No solipsist
has ever gone as far as this, and therefore every solipsist has been
inconsistent in accepting inferences about himself which have
no better warrant than inferences about other people and
things.

A very great deal of what we all unquestioningly accept as
knowledge depends upon testimony, and testimony, in turn,
depends upon the belief that there are other minds besides our
own. To common sense, the existence of other minds does not
appear open to doubt, and I do not myself see any reason to
disagree with common sense on this point. But, undoubtedly,
it is through experiences of my own that I am led to believe in
the minds of others; and, undoubtedly, as a matter of pure
logic, it would be possible for me to have these experiences even
if other minds did not exist. Part of our reason for believing in
other minds is derived from analogy, but part is derived from
another source which has a wider application. Suppose you
compare two copies of the same book and find that they agree
word for word, you cannot resist the conclusion that they have a
common cause, and you can trace this common cause backward
through compositors and publishers to the author. You do not
find it credible that the author's body went through the motions
of writing the book without his having any thoughts meanwhile. Such grounds for admitting other minds are not demonstrative in the logical sense. You might have experiences in a
dream which would be equally convincing while you still slept,
but which you would regard as misleading when you woke.
Such facts warrant a certain degree of doubtfulness, but usually
only a very small degree. In the immense majority of cases, they
justify you in accepting testimony if there is no evidence to the
contrary.

I come next to purely physical occurrences. Take, for example, our reason for believing in sound-waves. If a loud explosion occurs at some point, the time when different people hear it depends upon their distance from that point. We find it incredible that these different people, at different times, should all experience a loud noise, unless something had been happening in the intervening spaces. A system of events at places where there were ears, combined with a total absence of connected events elsewhere, strikes us as altogether too staccato to be credible. An even simpler example is the persistence of material objects. We cannot believe that Mount Everest ceases to exist when no one is seeing it, or that our room goes out with a pop when we leave it. There is no reason why we should believe such absurdities. The principles which lead us to reject them are essentially the same as those which lead us to believe that things have happened to us which we have now forgotten.

Not only science, but a great deal of common sense, is concerned, not with individual occurrences, but with general laws. Our knowledge of general laws, however, when it is empirical, is inferred, validly or invalidly, from our knowledge of a number of particular occurrences. "Dogs bark" is a general law, but it could not be known if people had not heard particular dogs barking on particular occasions. I found that our knowledge of such particular occurrences raises problems which some philosophers, notably the logical positivists, have not sufficiently considered. These problems, however, are not those involved in non-demonstrative inference, since the inferences with which we are concerned can only be justifiable in virtue of some general law such as you employ when, hearing a bark, you infer a dog. The laws that science seeks are, for the most part, in some sense causal. And this brings me to the question, "What do we mean by causal laws, and what evidence is there of their occurrence?"

It used to be the custom among philosophers to think that causal laws can be stated in the form "A causes B," interpreted as meaning that whenever an event of a certain kind A occurs, it is followed by an event of another specified kind, B. It was held by many that a causal sequence involves something more than invariability and must have some character that can be called "necessity." Many empiricists, however, denied this and thought that nothing was involved except invariable sequence. This whole point of view, however, could never have persisted among philosophers if they had had any acquaintance with science. Causal laws must be either not invariable or such as state only tendencies. In classical dynamics they take the form of differential equations, stating acceleration, not actual occurrences. In modern physics the laws have become statistical: they do not state what will happen in any particular case, but only different things, each of which will happen in an assigned proportion of cases. For such reasons, causation is no longer what it used to be in the books of old-fashioned philosophers. Nevertheless, it still retains an essential place. Take, for example, what we mean by a single "thing" which is more or less persistent. This "thing" must really consist of a series of sets of occurrences, each set characterizing what we may call a momentary state of the "thing." The states of the "thing" at different times are, often, though not always, connected by means of laws which can be stated without mentioning other "things." If this were not the case, scientific knowledge could never get a start. Unless we know something without knowing everything, it is obvious that we can never know something. And this applies, not only to particular events, but also to the laws connecting events. In physics, atoms and molecules persist for a time, and, if they did not, the conception of motion would become meaningless. A human body persists for a time, although the atoms and molecules of which it is composed are not always the same. A photon which travels from a star to a human eye persists throughout its journey, and, if it did not, we should not be able to state what we mean by seeing a star. But all these kinds of persistence are only usual, not invariable, and the causal laws with which science begins must state only an approximation to what usually happens. Whether, in the end, something more exact is attainable, we do not know. What I think we can say is something like this: given any event, there is usually, at any neighbouring time and in some neighbouring place, an event very like the given event; and, as a rule, it is possible to discover some law approximately determining its small difference from the given event. Some such principle is necessary to explain the approximate persistence of many "things," and also to explain the difference between perceiving A and perceiving B—for example, if A and B are stars, both of which we are seeing.

I give the name of "causal line" to a series of events having the property that from any one of them something can be inferred as to neighbouring events in the series. It is the fact that such causal lines exist which has made the conception of "things" useful to common sense, and the conception of "matter" useful to physics. It is the fact that such causal lines are approximate, impermanent, and not universal which has caused modern physics to regard the conception of "matter" as unsatisfactory.

There is another conception which seemed to me of great utility in non-demonstrative inference, namely that of "structure." It seems reasonable to suppose that, if you see red in one direction and blue in another, there is some difference between what is happening in the one direction and what is happening in the other. It follows that, though we may be compelled to admit that the external causes for our sensations of colour are not themselves coloured in the same sense in which our sensations are, nevertheless, when you see a pattern of colours, there must be a similar pattern in the causes of your sensations of colour. The conception of space-time structure as something which often remains constant, or approximately constant, throughout a series of causally connected events, is very important and very fruitful. Suppose, to take a very simple example, A reads aloud from a book and B takes down what he hears from dictation, and what A saw in the book is verbally identical with what B has written, it would be quite absurd to deny a causal connection between four sets of events—viz. (1) what is printed in the book, (2) the noises made by A in reading aloud, (3) the noises heard by B, and (4) the words written by B. The same sort of thing applies to the relation between a gramophone record and the music that it produces. Or, again, consider broadcasting, where sounds are transformed into electro-magnetic waves, and the electro-magnetic waves are transformed back into sound. It would be impossible for the spoken sounds and the heard sounds to resemble each other as closely as they do unless the intervening electro-magnetic waves had had a space-time structure very closely similar to that of the words, spoken and heard. There are, in nature, innumerable examples of complex structures transmitted causally throughout changes of intrinsic quality, such as those between sound and electro-magnetic waves in broadcasting. In fact, all visual and auditory perceptions have this character of transmitting structure but not intrinsic quality.

People unaccustomed to modern logic find it difficult to suppose that we can know about a space-time structure without knowing the qualities that compose it.. This is part of a larger aspect of knowledge. Unless we are to land ourselves in preposterous paradoxes, we shall find it necessary to admit that we may know such propositions as "all A is B" or "some A is B," without being able to give any instance of A—e.g., "all the numbers that I have never thought of and never shall think of are greater than a thousand." Although this proposition is undeniable, I should contradict myself if I attempted to give an instance. The same sort of thing applies to space-time structure in the purely physical world, where there is no reason to suppose that the qualities composing the structure bear any intrinsic resemblance to the qualities that I know in sensible experience.

The general principles necessary to validate scientific inferences are not susceptible of proof in any ordinary sense. They are distilled out by analysis from particular cases which seem totally obvious, like the one that I gave a moment ago in which A dictates to B. There is a gradual development from what I call "animal expectation" up to the most refined laws of quantum physics. The whole process starts from experiencing A and expecting B. An animal experiences a certain smell and expects the food to be good to eat. If its expectation were usually mistaken, it would die. Evolution and adaptation to environment cause expectations to be more often right than wrong, although the expectations go beyond anything logically demonstrable. Nature, we may say, has certain habits. The habits of animals must have a certain adaptation to the habits of nature if the animals are to survive.

This would be a poor argument if employed against Cartesian scepticism. But I do not think it is possible to get anywhere if we start from scepticism. We must start from a broad acceptance of whatever seems to be knowledge and is not rejected for some specific reason. Hypothetical scepticism is useful in logical dissection. It enables us to see how far we can get without this or that premiss—as, for example, we can inquire how much of geometry is possible without the axiom of parallels. But it is only for such purposes that hypothetical scepticism is useful.

Before explaining the exact epistemological function of the indemonstrable premisses of non-demonstrative inference something further must be said about induction.

Induction, as I said above, is not among the premisses of non-demonstrative inference. But this is not because it is not used; it is because in the form in which it is used it is not indemonstrable. Keynes, in his *Treatise on Probability*, made an extremely able investigation of the possibility of deriving induction from the mathematical theory of probability. The question that he had to investigate was this: given a number of instances of A's which are B's and no contrary instances, in what circumstances does the probability of the generalization "all A is B" approach certainty as a limit when the number of A's that are B's is continually increased? The conclusion that he arrives at is that two conditions must be fulfilled if this is to happen. The first and more important of these conditions is that, before we know any instances of A's that are B's, the generalization "all A is B" should have a finite probability on the basis of the remainder of our knowledge. The second condition is that the probability of our observing only favourable instances, if the generalization is false, should tend to zero as a limit when the number of inferences is sufficiently increased. This condition is found by Keynes to be satisfied if there is some probability short of certainty, say P, such that, given that the generalization is false and that $n-1$ A's have been found to be B's, the chance that the nth A will be found to be a B is always less than P provided n is sufficiently great.

The second of these two conditions is less important than the first and is also much less inconvenient. I shall concentrate attention upon the first of the two conditions.

How are we to know that some suggested generalization has a finite probability in its favour before we have examined any of the evidence for or against it? It is this that we must know if Keynes's argument is to give any high degree of probability to a generalization when we know a great many instances in its favour and none against it. The postulates at which I arrived by an analysis of instances of non-demonstrative inference were intended to be such as would confer this finite *a priori* probability upon certain generalizations and not upon others. It will be observed that, in order that the postulates in question should fulfil their function, it is not necessary that they should be certain; it is only necessary that they should have a finite probability. In this respect they differ very profoundly from the kind of *a priori* principles that idealistic philosophers have sought, for such principles have been supposed by their advocates to possess a certainty greater than that of most empirical knowledge.

The postulates at which I finally arrived were five. I do not lay any stress upon their exact formulation. I think it highly probable that their number could be reduced and that they could be stated with more precision. But, while I am not persuaded that they are all *necessary,* I do think they are *sufficient.* It should be noted that all of them state only probabilities, not certainties, and are designed only to confer that finite antecedent probability which Keynes needs to validate his inductions. I have already said something in a preliminary way about these postulates, but I will now repeat them more exactly and more explicitly.

The first of these I call "the postulate of quasi-permanence," which may be regarded, in a sense, as replacing Newton's first law of motion. It is in virtue of this postulate that common sense is able to operate more or less successfully with the concept of "persons" and the concept of "things." It is also in virtue of this postulate that science and philosophy were able, for a long time, to make use of the concept of "substance." What the postulate states is as follows:

Given any event A, it happens very frequently that, at any neighbouring time, there is at some neighbouring place an event very similar to A.

This very similar event will be regarded by common sense as part of the history of the person or thing to whom the event A happened.

The second postulate is that of separable causal lines. This is perhaps the most important of all the five. It enables us, from partial knowledge, to make a partial probable inference. We believe that everything in the universe has, or may have, *some* effect upon everything else, and since we do not know everything in the universe, we cannot tell exactly and certainly what will happen to anything; but we can tell approximately and with probability; and if we could not, knowledge and scientific laws could never get started. The postulate is as follows:

It is frequently possible to form a series of events such that, from one or two members of the series, something can be inferred as to all the other members.

The most obvious examples are such things as sound waves and light waves. It is owing to the permanence of such waves that hearing and sight can give us information about more or less distant occurrences.

The third postulate is that of spatio-temporal continuity, which is mainly concerned to deny action at a distance. It maintains that, when there is a causal connection between two events that are not contiguous, there must be intermediate links in the causal chain. For example, if A hears what B says, we think that some process must have intervened between A and B. I do not feel sure, however, that this postulate could not be reduced to a tautology, since physical space-time is entirely inferential and the ordering of space-time events is dependent upon causality.

The fourth postulate, which I call "the structural postulate," is very important and very fruitful. It is concerned with such cases as a number of people hearing the same speech or seeing the same performance in a theatre or, to take an example with wider scope, seeing the same stars in the sky. What the postulate says is as follows:

When a number of structurally similar complex events are ranged about a centre in regions not widely separated, it is usually the case that all belong to causal lines having their origin in an event of the same structure at the centre.

The importance of space-time structure, which I first emphasized in *The Analysis of Matter*, is very great. It explains how one complex event can be causally connected with another complex event, although they are not in any way qualitatively similar. They need only resemble each other in the abstract properties of their space-time structure. It is obvious that the electro-magnetic waves used in broadcasting cause the sensations of the hearers, but do not resemble them except in structural respects. It is because of the importance of structure that theoretical physics is able to content itself with formulae that are about unexperienced occurrences which need not, except in structure, resemble any of the occurrences that we experience.

The last postulate is that of analogy, the most important function of which is to justify the belief in other minds. The postulate is as follows:

Given two classes of events A and B, and given that, whenever both A and B can be observed, there is reason to believe that A causes B, then if, in a given case, A is observed, but there is no way of observing whether B occurs or not, it is probable that B occurs; and similarly if B is observed, but the presence or absence of A cannot be observed.

The above postulates, I repeat, are justified by the fact that they are implied in inferences which we all accept as valid, and that, although they cannot be proved in any formal sense, the whole system of science and everyday knowledge, out of which they have been distilled, is, within limits, self-confirmatory. I do not accept the coherence theory of *truth*, but there is a coherence theory of *probability* which is important and I think valid. Suppose you have two facts and a causal principle which connects them, the probability of all three may be greater than the probability of any one, and the more numerous and complex the inter-connected facts and principles become, the greater is the increase of probability derived from their mutual coherence. It is to be observed that, without the introduction of principles, no suggested collection of facts, or supposed facts, is either coherent or inconsistent, since no two facts can either imply or contradict each other except in virtue of some extralogical principle. I believe that the above five principles, or something analogous to them, can form the basis for the kind of coherence which gives rise to the increased probability with which we have been concerned. Something vaguely called "causality" or "the uniformity of nature" appears in many discussions of scientific method. The purpose of my postulates is to substitute something more precise and more effective in place of such rather vague principles. I feel no great confidence in the precise postulates above enumerated, but I feel considerable confidence that something of the same sort is necessary if we are to justify the non-demonstrative inferences concerning which none of us, in fact, can feel any doubt.

Ever since I was engaged on *Principia Mathematica*, I have had a certain method of which at first I was scarcely conscious, but which has gradually become more explicit in my thinking. The method consists in an attempt to build a bridge between the world of sense and the world of science. I accept both as, in broad outline, not to be questioned. As in making a tunnel through an Alpine mountain, work must proceed from both ends in the hope that at last the labour will be crowned by a meeting in the middle.

Let us begin with the analysis of some body of scientific knowledge. All scientific knowledge uses artificially manufactured entities of which the purpose is to be easily manipulated by the methods of some calculus. The more advanced the science, the more true this is. Among empirical sciences, it is most completely true in physics. In an advanced science, such as physics, there is, for the philosopher, a preliminary labour of exhibiting the science as a deductive system starting with certain principles from which the rest follows logically and with certain real or supposed entities in terms of which everything dealt with by the science in question can, at least theoretically, be defined. If this labour has been adequately performed, the principles and entities, which remain as the residue after analysis, can be taken as hostages for the whole science in question, and the philosopher need no longer concern himself with the rest of the complicated knowledge which constitutes that science.

But no empirical science is intended merely as a coherent fairy-tale. It is intended to consist of statements having application to the real world and believed because of their relation to that world. Even the most abstract parts of science, such, for instance, as the general theory of relativity, are accepted because of observed facts. The philosopher is thus compelled to investigate the relation between observed facts and scientific abstractions. This is a long and arduous task. One of the reasons for its difficulty is that common sense, which is our starting-point, is already infected with theory, though of a crude and primitive kind. What we think that we observe is more than what we in fact observe, the "more" being added by common-sense metaphysics and science. I am not suggesting that we should wholly reject the metaphysics and science of common sense, but only that it is part of what we have to examine. It does not belong to either of the two poles of formulated science, on the one hand, or unmixed observation, on the other.

I have been much criticized for applying the methods of mathematical logic to the interpretation of physics, but, in this matter, I am wholly unrepentant. It was Whitehead who first showed me what was possible in this field. Mathematical physics works with a space composed of points, a time composed of instants and a matter composed of punctual particles. No modern mathematical physicist supposes that there are such things in nature. But it is possible, given a higgledy-piggledy collection of things destitute of the smooth properties that mathematicians like, to make structures composed of these things and having the properties which are convenient to the mathematician. It is because this is possible that mathematical physics is more than an idle amusement. And it is mathematical logic which shows how such structures are to be made. For this reason, mathematical logic is an essential tool in constructing the bridge between sense and science of which I spoke above.

The method of Cartesian doubt, which appealed to me when I was young and may still serve as a tool in the work of logical dissection, no longer seems to me to have fundamental validity. Universal scepticism cannot be refuted, but also cannot be accepted. I have come to accept the facts of sense and the broad truth of science as things which the philosopher should take as data, since, though their truth is not quite certain, it has a higher degree of probability than anything likely to be achieved in philosophical speculation.

In the transition from crude fact to science, we need forms of inference additional to those of deductive logic. Traditionally, it was supposed that induction would serve this purpose, but this was an error, since it can be shown that the conclusions of inductive inferences from true premises are more often false than true. The principles of inference required for the transition from sense to science are to be attained by analysis. The analysis involved is that of the kinds of inference which nobody, in fact, questions: as, for example, that if, at one moment, you see your cat on the hearth-rug and, at another, you see it in a doorway, it has passed over intermediate positions although you did not see it doing so. If the work of analysing scientific inference has been properly performed, it will appear that concrete instances of such inference are (a) such as no one honestly doubts, and (b) such as are essential if, on the basis of sensible facts, we are to believe things which go beyond this basis.

The outcome of such work is to be regarded rather as science than as philosophy. That is to say, the reasons for accepting it are the ordinary reasons applied in scientific work, not remote reasons derived from some metaphysical theory. More especially, there is no such claim to certainty as has, too often and too uselessly, been made by rash philosophers.

PART SIX

PART SIX

Science and Culture

Science, both as an activity and as a body of knowledge,
has an important role in human life. Russell has always
been keenly aware of this, and for over half a century has
written on the relation of science to other important human concerns. Sometimes he is optimistic over the benefits
that science can bring, sometimes deeply disturbed by what
he considers the misuses of science, or by misunderstand-
ings of the true nature of scientific knowledge. Part Six
contains writings from two areas in which the effects of
science especially interest him.

Chapter One is an essay on the place of science in a
liberal education, an eloquent statement by Russell that
far from being opposed to the aims of a liberal education,
science has an essential place in their realization.

Chapter Two is one of Russell's recent statements on the
role of science and scientists in political and social affairs.

CHAPTER ONE

The Place of Science in a
Liberal Education

Science, to the ordinary reader of newspapers, is represented by
a varying selection of sensational triumphs, such as wireless
telegraphy and aeroplanes, radio-activity and the marvels of
modern alchemy. It is not of this aspect of science that I wish
to speak. Science, in this aspect, consists of detached up-to-date
fragments, interesting only until they are replaced by something
newer and more up-to-date, displaying nothing of the systems
of patiently constructed knowledge out of which, almost as a
casual incident, have come the practically useful results which
interest the man in the street. The increased command over the
forces of nature which is derived from science is undoubtedly
an amply sufficient reason for encouraging scientific research,
but this reason has been so often urged and is so easily appre-
ciated that other reasons, to my mind quite as important, are
apt to be overlooked. It is with these other reasons, especially
with the intrinsic value of a scientific habit of mind in forming
our outlook on the world, that I shall be concerned in what
follows.

The instance of wireless telegraphy will serve to illustrate
the difference between the two points of view. Almost all the
serious intellectual labour required for the possibility of this

From *Mysticism and Logic* by Bertrand Russell (1st edn., 1918, 2nd edn.,
1929), Chapter II, pp. 33-45. Reprinted by permission of the publishers,
George Allen & Unwin Ltd., London. This selection originally appeared in
The New Statesman and Nation, Vol. I, May 24 and 31, 1913.

invention is due to three men—Faraday, Maxwell, and Hertz. In alternating layers of experiment and theory these three men built up the modern theory of electromagnetism, and demonstrated the identity of light with electromagnetic waves. The system which they discovered is one of profound intellectual interest, bringing together and unifying an endless variety of apparently detached phenomena, and displaying a cumulative mental power which cannot but afford delight to every generous spirit. The mechanical details which remained to be adjusted in order to utilise their discoveries for a practical system of telegraphy demanded, no doubt, very considerable ingenuity, but had not that broad sweep and that universality which could give them intrinsic interest as an object of disinterested contemplation.

From the point of view of training the mind, of giving that well-informed, impersonal outlook which constitutes culture in the good sense of this much-misused word, it seems to be generally held indisputable that a literary education is superior to one based on science. Even the warmest advocates of science are apt to rest their claims on the contention that culture ought to be sacrificed to utility. Those men of science who respect culture, when they associate with men learned in the classics, are apt to admit, not merely politely, but sincerely, a certain inferiority on their side, compensated doubtless by the services which science renders to humanity, but none the less real. And so long as this attitude exists among men of science, it tends to verify itself: the intrinsically valuable aspects of science tend to be sacrificed to the merely useful, and little attempt is made to preserve that leisurely, systematic survey by which the finer quality of mind is formed and nourished.

But even if there be, in present fact, any such inferiority as is supposed in the educational value of science, this is, I believe, not the fault of science itself, but the fault of the spirit in which science is taught. If its full possibilities were realised by those who teach it, I believe that its capacity of producing those habits of mind which constitute the highest mental excellence would be at least as great as that of literature, and more particularly of Greek and Latin literature. In saying this I have no wish whatever to disparage a classical education. I have not myself enjoyed its benefits, and my knowledge of Greek and Latin authors is derived almost wholly from translations. But I am firmly persuaded that the Greeks fully deserve all the admiration that is bestowed upon them, and that it is a very great and serious loss to be unacquainted with their writings. It is not by attacking them, but by drawing attention to neg-lected excellences in science, that I wish to conduct my argument.

One defect, however, does seem inherent in a purely classical education—namely, a too exclusive emphasis on the past. By the study of what is absolutely ended and can never be renewed, a habit of criticism towards the present and the future is en-gendered. The qualities in which the present excels are qualities to which the study of the past does not direct attention, and to which, therefore, the student of Greek civilisation may easily become blind. In what is new and growing there is apt to be something crude, insolent, even a little vulgar, which is shock-ing to the man of sensitive taste; quivering from the rough contact, he retires to the trim gardens of a polished past, for-getting that they were reclaimed from the wilderness by men as rough and earth-soiled as those from whom he shrinks in his own day. The habit of being unable to recognise merit until it is dead is too apt to be the result of a purely bookish life, and a culture based wholly on the past will seldom be able to pierce through everyday surroundings to the essential splendour of contemporary things, or to the hope of still greater splendour in the future.

> My eyes saw not the men of old;
> And now their age away has rolled.
> I weep—to think I shall not see
> The heroes of posterity.

So says the Chinese poet; but such impartiality is rare in the more pugnacious atmosphere of the West, where the champions of past and future fight a never-ending battle, instead of com-bining to seek out the merits of both.

This consideration, which militates not only against the exclusive study of the classics, but against every form of culture which has become static, traditional, and academic, leads inevitably to the fundamental question: What is the true end of education? But before attempting to answer this question it will be well to define the sense in which we are to use the word "education." For this purpose I shall distinguish the sense in which I mean to use it from two others, both perfectly legitimate, the one broader and the other narrower than the sense in which I mean to use the word.

In the broader sense, education will include not only what we learn through instruction, but all that we learn through personal experience—the formation of character through the education of life. Of this aspect of education, vitally important as it is, I will say nothing, since its consideration would introduce topics quite foreign to the question with which we are concerned.

In the narrower sense, education may be confined to instruction, the imparting of definite information on various subjects, because such information, in and for itself, is useful in daily life. Elementary education—reading, writing, and arithmetic—is almost wholly of this kind. But instruction, necessary as it is, does not *per se* constitute education in the sense in which I wish to consider it.

Education, in the sense in which I mean it, may be defined as *the formation, by means of instruction, of certain mental habits and a certain outlook on life and the world.* It remains to ask ourselves, what mental habits, and what sort of outlook, can be hoped for as the result of instruction? When we have answered this question we can attempt to decide what science has to contribute to the formation of the habits and outlook which we desire.

Our whole life is built about a certain number—not a very small number—of primary instincts and impulses. Only what is in some way connected with these instincts and impulses appears to us desirable or important; there is no faculty, whether "reason" or "virtue" or whatever it may be called, that can take our active life and our hopes and fears outside the region controlled by these first movers of all desire. Each of them is like a queen-bee, aided by a hive of workers gathering honey; but when the queen is gone the workers languish and die, and the cells remain empty of their expected sweetness. So with each primary impulse in civilised man: it is surrounded and protected by a busy swarm of attendant derivative desires, which store up in its service whatever honey the surrounding world affords. But if the queen-impulse dies, the death-dealing influence, though retarded a little by habit, spreads slowly through all the subsidiary impulses, and a whole tract of life becomes inexplicably colourless. What was formerly full of zest, and so obviously worth doing that it raised no questions, has now grown dreary and purposeless: with a sense of disillusion we inquire the meaning of life, and decide, perhaps, that all is vanity. The search for an outside meaning that can *compel* an inner response must always be disappointed: all "meaning" must be at bottom related to our primary desires, and when they are extinct no miracle can restore to the world the value which they reflected upon it.

The purpose of education, therefore, cannot be to create any primary impulse which is lacking in the uneducated; the purpose can only be to enlarge the scope of those that human nature provides, by increasing the number and variety of attendant thoughts, and by showing where the most permanent satisfaction is to be found. Under the impulse of a Calvinistic horror of the "natural man" this obvious truth has been too often misconceived in the training of the young; "nature" has been falsely regarded as excluding all that is best in what is natural, and the endeavour to teach virtue has led to the production of stunted and contorted hypocrites instead of full-grown human beings. From such mistakes in education a better psychology or a kinder heart is beginning to preserve the present generation; we need, therefore, waste no more words on the theory that the purpose of education is to thwart or eradicate nature.

But although nature must supply the initial force of desire, nature is not, in the civilised man, the spasmodic, fragmentary, and yet violent set of impulses that it is in the savage. Each impulse has its constitutional ministry of thought and knowledge and reflection, through which possible conflicts of impulses are foreseen, and temporary impulses are controlled by the unifying impulse which may be called wisdom. In this way education destroys the crudity of instinct, and increases through knowledge the wealth and variety of the individual's contacts with the outside world, making him no longer an isolated fighting unit, but a citizen of the universe, embracing distant countries, remote regions of space, and vast stretches of past and future within the circle of his interests. It is this simultaneous softening in the insistence of desire and enlargement of its scope that is the chief moral end of education.

Closely connected with this moral end is the more purely intellectual aim of education, the endeavour to make us see and imagine the world in an objective manner, as far as possible as it is in itself, and not merely through the distorting medium of personal desire. The complete attainment of such an objective view is no doubt an ideal, indefinitely approachable, but not actually and fully realisable. Education, considered as a process of forming our mental habits and our outlook on the world, is to be judged successful in proportion as its outcome approximates to this ideal; in proportion, that is to say, as it gives us a true view of our place in society, of the relation of the whole human society to its non-human environment, and of the nature of the non-human world as it is in itself apart from our desires and interests. If this standard is admitted, we can return to the consideration of science, inquiring how far science contributes to such an aim, and whether it is in any respect superior to its rivals in educational practice.

II

Two opposite and at first sight conflicting merits belong to science as against literature and art. The one, which is not inherently necessary, but is certainly true at the present day, is hopefulness as to the future of human achievement, and in particular as to the useful work that may be accomplished by any intelligent student. This merit and the cheerful outlook which it engenders prevent what might otherwise be the depressing effect of another aspect of science, to my mind also a merit, and perhaps its greatest merit—I mean the irrelevance of human passions and of the whole subjective apparatus where scientific truth is concerned. Each of these reasons for preferring the study of science requires some amplification. Let us begin with the first.

In the study of literature or art our attention is perpetually riveted upon the past: the men of Greece or of the Renaissance did better than any men do now; the triumphs of former ages, so far from facilitating fresh triumphs in our own age, actually increase the difficulty of fresh triumphs by rendering originality harder of attainment; not only is artistic achievement not cumulative, but it seems even to depend upon a certain freshness and *naïveté* of impulse and vision which civilisation tends to destroy. Hence comes, to those who have been nourished on the literary and artistic productions of former ages, a certain peevishness and undue fastidiousness towards the present, from which there seems no escape except into the deliberate vandalism which ignores tradition and in the search after originality achieves only the eccentric. But in such vandalism there is none of the simplicity and spontaneity out of which great art springs: theory is still the canker in its core, and insincerity destroys the advantages of a merely pretended ignorance.

The despair thus arising from an education which suggests no pre-eminent mental activity except that of artistic creation is wholly absent from an education which gives the knowledge of scientific method. The discovery of scientific method, except in pure mathematics, is a thing of yesterday; speaking broadly, we may say that it dates from Galileo. Yet already it has transformed the world, and its success proceeds with ever-accelerating velocity. In science men have discovered an activity of the very highest value in which they are no longer, as in art, dependent for progress upon the appearance of continually greater genius, for in science the successors stand upon the shoulders of their predecessors; where one man of supreme genius has invented a method, a thousand lesser men can apply it. No transcendent ability is required in order to make useful discoveries in science; the edifice of science needs its masons, bricklayers, and common labourers as well as its foremen, master-builders, and architects. In art nothing worth doing can be done without genius; in science even a very moderate capacity can contribute to a supreme achievement.

In science the man of real genius is the man who invents a new method. The notable discoveries are often made by his successors, who can apply the method with fresh vigour, unimpaired by the previous labour of perfecting it; but the mental calibre of the thought required for their work, however brilliant, is not so great as that required by the first inventor of the method. There are in science immense numbers of different methods, appropriate to different classes of problems; but over and above them all, there is something not easily definable, which may be called *the* method of science. It was formerly customary to identify this with the inductive method, and to associate it with the name of Bacon. But the true inductive method was not discovered by Bacon, and the true method of science is something which includes deduction as much as induction, logic and mathematics as much as botany and geology. I shall not attempt the difficult task of stating what the scientific method is, but I will try to indicate the temper of mind out of which the scientific method grows, which is the second of the two merits that were mentioned above as belonging to a scientific education.

The kernel of the scientific outlook is a thing so simple, so obvious, so seemingly trivial, that the mention of it may almost excite derision. The kernel of the scientific outlook is the refusal to regard our own desires, tastes, and interests as affording a key to the understanding of the world. Stated thus baldly, this may seem no more than a trite truism. But to remember it consistently in matters arousing our passionate partisanship is by no means easy, especially where the available evidence is uncertain and inconclusive. A few illustrations will make this clear.

Aristotle, I understand, considered that the stars must move in circles because the circle is the most perfect curve. In the absence of evidence to the contrary, he allowed himself to decide a question of fact by an appeal to æsthetico-moral considerations. In such a case it is at once obvious to us that this appeal was unjustifiable. We know now how to ascertain as a fact the way in which the heavenly bodies move, and we know that they do not move in circles, or even in accurate ellipses, or in any other kind of simply describable curve. This may be painful to a certain hankering after simplicity of pattern in the universe, but we know that in astronomy such feelings are irrelevant. Easy as this knowledge seems now, we owe it to the courage and insight of the first inventors of scientific method, and more especially of Galileo.

We may take as another illustration Malthus's doctrine of population. This illustration is all the better for the fact that his actual doctrine is now known to be largely erroneous. It is not his conclusions that are valuable, but the temper and method of his inquiry. As everyone knows, it was to him that Darwin owed an essential part of his theory of natural selection, and this was only possible because Malthus's outlook was truly scientific. His great merit lies in considering man not as the object of praise or blame, but as a part of nature, a thing with a certain characteristic behaviour from which certain consequences must follow. If the behaviour is not quite what Malthus supposed, if the consequences are not quite what he inferred, that many falsify his conclusions, but does not impair the value of his method. The objections which were made when his doctrine was new—that it was horrible and depressing, that people ought not to act as he said they did, and so on—were all such as implied an unscientific attitude of mind; as against all of them, his calm determination to treat man as a natural phenomenon marks an important advance over the reformers of the eighteenth century and the Revolution.

Under the influence of Darwinism the scientific attitude towards man has now become fairly common, and is to some people quite natural, though to most it is still a difficult and artificial intellectual contortion. There is, however, one study which is as yet almost wholly untouched by the scientific spirit —I mean the study of philosophy. Philosophers and the public imagine that the scientific spirit must pervade pages that bristle with allusions to ions, germ-plasms, and the eyes of shell-fish. But as the devil can quote Scripture, so the philosopher can quote science. The scientific spirit is not an affair of quotation, of externally acquired information, any more than manners are an affair of the etiquette-book. The scientific attitude of mind involves a sweeping away of all other desires in the interests of the desire to know—it involves suppression of hopes and fears, loves and hates, and the whole subjective emotional life, until we become subdued to the material, able to see it frankly, without preconceptions, without bias, without any wish except to see it as it is, and without any belief that what it is must be determined by some relation, positive or negative, to what we should like it to be, or to what we can easily imagine it to be.

Now in philosophy this attitude of mind has not as yet been achieved. A certain self-absorption, not personal, but human, has marked almost all attempts to conceive the universe as a whole. Mind, or some aspect of it—thought or will or sentience —has been regarded as the pattern after which the universe is to be conceived, for no better reason, at bottom, than that such a universe would not seem strange, and would give us the cosy feeling that every place is like home. To conceive the universe as essentially progressive or essentially deteriorating, for example, is to give to our hopes and fears a cosmic importance which *may*, of course, be justified, but which we have as yet no reason to suppose justified. Until we have learnt to think of it in ethically neutral terms, we have not arrived at a scientific attitude in philosophy; and until we have arrived at such an attitude, it is hardly to be hoped that philosophy will achieve any solid results.

I have spoken so far largely of the negative aspect of the scientific spirit, but it is from the positive aspect that its value is derived. The instinct of constructiveness, which is one of the chief incentives to artistic creation, can find in scientific systems a satisfaction more massive than any epic poem. Disinterested curiosity, which is the source of almost all intellectual effort, finds with astonished delight that science can unveil secrets which might well have seemed forever undiscoverable. The desire for a larger life and wider interests, for an escape from private circumstances, and even from the whole recurring human cycle of birth and death, is fulfilled by the impersonal cosmic outlook of science as by nothing else. To all these must be added, as contributing to the happiness of the man of science, the admiration of splendid achievement, and the consciousness of inestimable utility to the human race. A life devoted to science is therefore a happy life, and its happiness is derived from the very best sources that are open to dwellers on this troubled and passionate planet.

CHAPTER TWO

Science and Human Life

Science and the techniques to which it has given rise have changed human life during the last hundred and fifty years more than it had been changed since men took to agriculture, and the changes that are being wrought by science continue at an increasing speed. There is no sign of any new stability to be attained on some scientific plateau. On the contrary, there is every reason to think that the revolutionary possibilities of science extend immeasurably beyond what has so far been realized. Can the human race adjust itself quickly enough to these vertiginous transformations, or will it, as innumerable former species have done, perish from lack of adaptability? The dinosaurs were, in their day, the lords of creation, and if there had been philosophers among them not one would have foreseen that the whole race might perish. But they became extinct because they could not adapt themselves to a world without swamps. In the case of man and science, there is a wholly new factor, namely that man himself is creating the changes of environment to which he will have to adjust himself with unprecedented rapidity. But, although man through his scientific skill is the cause of the changes of environment, most of these changes are not willed by human beings. Although they come about through human agencies, they have, or at any rate have had so far, something of the inexorable inevitability of natural forces. Whether Nature dried up the swamps or men deliberately drained them, makes little difference as regards the ultimate result. Whether men will be able to survive the changes of environment that their own skill has brought about is an open question. If the answer is in the affirmative, it will be known some day; if not, not. If the answer is to be in the affirmative, men will have to apply scientific ways of thinking to themselves and their institutions. They cannot continue to hope, as all politicians hitherto have, that in a world where everything has changed, the political and social habits of the eighteenth century can remain inviolate. Not only will men of science have to grapple with the sciences that deal with man, but—and this is a far more difficult matter—they will have to persuade the world to listen to what they have discovered. If they cannot succeed in this difficult enterprise, man will destroy himself by his halfway cleverness. I am told that, if he were out of the way, the future would lie with rats. I hope they will find it a pleasant world, but I am glad I shall not be there.

But let us pass from these generalities to more specific questions.

One of the most obvious problems raised by a scientific technique is that of the exhaustion of the soil and of raw materials. This subject has been much discussed, and some governments have actually taken some steps to prevent the denudation of the soil. But I doubt whether, as yet, the good done by these measures is outweighing the harm done in less careful regions. Food, however, is such an obvious necessity that the problem is bound to receive increasing attention as population pressure makes it more urgent. Whether this increased attention will do good or harm in the long run is, I fear, questionable. By a spendthrift use of fertilizers, food production in the present can be increased at the cost of food production in the future. Can you imagine a politician going to his constituents and saying: "Ladies and gentlemen, it is in your power to have abundance of food for the next thirty years, but the measures that will give you this abundance will cause scarcity for your grandchildren. I am therefore proposing measures to insure frugality in the present in order to avoid famine in the somewhat distant future." Is it possible to believe that a politician who said this would win elections against one less addicted to foresight? I hardly think so, unless the general level of political intelligence and virtue can be very considerably increased.

The question of raw materials is more difficult and complex than the question of food. The raw materials required at one stage of technique are different from those required at another. It may be that by the time the world's supply of oil is exhausted, atomic power will have taken its place. But to this sort of process there is a limit, though not an easily assignable one. At present there is a race for uranium, and it would seem likely that before very long there will be no easily accessible source of uranium. If, when that happens, the world has come to depend upon nuclear energy as its main source of power, the result may be devastating. All such speculations are of course very questionable, since new techniques may always make it possible to dispense with formerly necessary raw materials. But we cannot get away from the broad fact that we are living upon the world's capital of stored energy and are transforming the energy at a continually increasing rate into forms in which it cannot be utilized. Such a manner of life can hardly be stable, but must sooner or later bring the penalty that lies in wait for those who live on capital.

In primitive times, when the human population of the globe was small, such problems did not arise. Agriculture, it is true, was practiced in ways that exhausted the soil for a time, but there were usually new vacant lands available; and if there were not, the corpses of enemies sufficed as fertilizers. The system was "conservative" in the physicists' sense. That is to say, energy on the whole accumulated as fast as it was used. Now, this is not the case; and, so far as one can see, it will never be the case while scientific technique continues.

All this however, you may say, is distant and doubtful: we have more pressing matters to consider. This is true, and I will proceed to consider some of them.

The problem which most preoccupies the public mind at the

present moment is that of scientific warfare. It has become evident that, if scientific skill is allowed free scope, the human race will be exterminated, if not in the next war, then in the next but one or the next but two—at any rate at no very distant date. To this problem there are two possible reactions: there are those who say, "let us create social institutions which will make large-scale war impossible"; there are others who say, "let us not allow war to become *too* scientific. We cannot perhaps go back to bows and arrows, but let us at any rate agree with our enemies that, if we fight them, both sides will fight inefficiently." For my part, I favor the former answer, since I cannot see that either side could be expected to observe an agreement not to use modern weapons if once war had broken out. It is on this ground that I do not think that there will long continue to be human beings unless methods are found of permanently preventing large-scale wars. But this is a serious question as to which I will say no more at the moment. I shall return to it presently.

The substitution of machines for human labor raises problems which are likely to become acute in the not very distant future. These problems are not new. They began with the Industrial Revolution, which ruined large numbers of skilled and industrious handicraftsmen, inflicting upon them hardships that they had in no way deserved and that they bitterly resented. But their troubles were transitory: they died; and such of their children as survived sought other occupations. The sufferers had no political power and were not able to offer any effective resistance to "progress." Nowadays, in democratic countries, the political situation is different and wage earners cannot be expected to submit tamely to starvation. But if we are to believe Norbert Wiener's book on cybernetics—and I see no reason why we should not—it should soon be possible to keep up the existing level of production with a very much smaller number of workers. The more economical methods, one may suppose, would be introduced during a war while the workers were at the front, if such a war were not quickly ended by H-bomb extermination, and when the survivors returned their former

jobs would no longer be available. The social discontent resulting from such a situation would be very grave. It could be dealt
with in a totalitarian country, but a democracy could only deal
with it by radical changes in its social philosophy and even in its
ethics. Work has been thought to be a duty, but in such a
situation there would be little work to do and duty would have
to take new forms.

Changes in political philosophy are necessary for several reasons. One of the most important is that modern techniques
make society more organic in the sense that its parts are more
interdependent and an injury to one individual or group is
more likely than it formerly was to cause injury to other individuals or groups. It is easier to kill a man than to kill a sponge
because he is more highly organized and more centralized. In
like manner it is easier to inflict vital damage upon a scientific
community than upon a community of nomads or scattered
peasants. This increase of interdependence makes it necessary
to limit freedom in various ways which liberals in the past considered undesirable. There are two spheres in which such limitation is especially necessary: the one is in economics; and the
other, in the relations between states.

Take economics first. Suppose, as is not improbable, that most
of the power used in industry comes to be distributed from a
fairly small number of atomic power-stations, and suppose that
the men working in these stations retained the right to strike.
They could completely paralyze the industrial life of a nation
and could levy almost unlimited blackmail in the form of demands for higher wages. No community would tolerate such
a state of affairs. The workers in power-stations would have to
have understudies like actors in a theater, and the forces of the
state would have to be employed if necessary to enable the
understudies to replace workers on strike. Another example,
which war has already brought to the fore, is the supply and
use of raw materials. Whenever raw materials are scarce their
distribution has to be controlled and not left to the free play
of unfettered economic forces. Scarcity of this sort has hitherto
been thought of as a transitory phenomenon due to the needs

and ravages of war. But it is likely to remain, in regard to many essentials, a normal condition of highly developed industry. Some central authority for the allocation of raw materials must therefore be expected as a necessary limitation of economic freedom. Another unavoidable limitation comes from the vastness of some obviously desirable enterprises. To bring fertility to the interior of Australia and to parts of Siberia is almost certainly possible, but only by an expenditure far beyond the capacity of private enterprise. One may expect that the progress of science will increase the number of such possible enterprises. Perhaps it will be possible in time to make the Sahara rainy, or even to make northern Canada warm. But, if such things become possible, they will be possible only for whole communities and not for private corporations.

Even more important than the limitations of economic liberty are the limitations on the liberty of states. The liberal doctrine of nationality, which was preached by liberals before 1848 and embodied in the Treaty of Versailles by President Wilson, had its justification as a protest against alien domination. But to allow *complete* liberty to any national state is just as anarchic as it would be to allow complete liberty to an individual. There are things which an individual must not do because the criminal law forbids them. The law and the police are in most cases strong enough to prevent such things from being done: murderers are a very small percentage of the population of any civilized country. But the relations between states are not governed by law and cannot be until there is a supranational armed force strong enough to enforce the decisions of a supranational authority. In the past, although the wars resulting from international anarchy caused much suffering and destruction, mankind was able to survive them, and, on the whole, the risks of war were thought less irksome than the controls that would be necessary to prevent it. This is ceasing to be true. The risks of war have become so great that the continued existence of our species either has become or soon will become incompatible with the new methods of scientific destruction.

The new dangers resulting from our more organic society

call for certain changes in the kind of character that is admired. The bold buccaneer, or the great conqueror such as Alexander or Napoleon, has been admired and is still admired although the world can no longer afford this type of character. We come here upon a difficulty. It is a good thing that people should be adventurous and that there should be scope for individual enterprise; but the adventure and enterprise, if they are not to bring total disaster, must steer clear of certain fields in which they were formerly possible. You may still, without harm to your fellow men, wish to be the first man to reach the moon. You may wish to be a great poet or a great composer or a man who advances the boundaries of scientific knowledge. Such adventure injures no one. But if Napoleon is your ideal, you must be restrained. Certain kinds of anarchic self-assertion, which are splendid in the literature of tragedy, have come to involve too much risk. A motorist alone on an empty road may drive as he pleases, but in crowded traffic he must obey the rules. More and more the lives of individuals come to resemble the motorist in traffic rather than the lonely driver in an empty desert.

I come at last to a question which is causing considerable concern and perplexity to many men of science, namely: what is their social duty toward this new world that they have been creating? I do not think this question is easy or simple. The pure man of science, as such, is concerned with the advancement of knowledge, and in his professional moments he takes it for granted that the advancement of knowledge is desirable. But inevitably he finds himself casting his pearls before swine. Men who do not understand his scientific work can utilize the knowledge that he provides. The new techniques to which it gives rise often have totally unexpected effects. The men who decide what use shall be made of the new techniques are not necessarily possessed of any exceptional degree of wisdom. They are mainly politicians whose professional skill consists in knowing how to play upon the emotions of masses of men. The emotions which easily sway masses are very seldom the best of which the individuals composing the masses are capable. And so the scientist finds that he has unintentionally placed new powers in the hands of reckless men. He may easily come to doubt, in moments of depression or overwork, whether the world would not be a happier place if science did not exist. He knows that science gives power and that the power which it gives could be used to increase human welfare; but he knows also that very often it is used, not so, but in the very opposite direction. Is he on this account to view himself as an unintentional malefactor?

I do not think so. I think we must retain the belief that scientific knowledge is one of the glories of man. I will not maintain that knowledge can never do harm. I think such general propositions can almost always be refuted by well-chosen examples. What I will maintain—and maintain vigorously—is that knowledge is very much more often useful than harmful and that fear of knowledge is very much more often harmful than useful. Suppose you are a scientific pioneer and you make some discovery of great scientific importance, and suppose you say to yourself, "I am afraid this discovery will do harm": you know that other people are likely to make the same discovery if they are allowed suitable opportunities for research; you must therefore, if you do not wish the discovery to become public, either discourage your sort of research or control publication by a board of censors. Nine times out of ten, the board of censors will object to knowledge that is in fact useful—e.g., knowledge concerning contraceptives—rather than to knowledge that would in fact be harmful. It is very difficult to foresee the social effects of new knowledge, and it is very easy from the sheer force of habit to shrink from new knowledge such as might promote new kinds of behavior.

Apart from the more general duties of scientists toward society, they have a quite special and exceptional duty in the present critical condition of the world. All men of science who have studied thermonuclear warfare are aware of two superlatively important facts: first, that whatever agreements may have been reached to the contrary, thermonuclear weapons will certainly be employed by both sides in a world war; second, that if such weapons are employed there can be no hope of victory for either side, but only of universal destruction involving, quite possibly, the end of all human and animal life and almost certainly, failing that, a complete reversion to barbarism. A great war with thermonuclear weapons will not produce a universal victory of communism. It will also not produce the sort of world desired by the Western Powers. Nor will it give opportunity for the independent flourishing of Southeast Asia or Africa. Radioactive clouds, borne by the wind, will not respect frontiers and will ignore the legal rights of neutrals. In view of this prospect, there is one matter upon which the interests of the whole world coincide. Whether you are a Communist or an anti-Communist, an inhabitant of Asia or Europe or America, a white, brown, yellow or black man, your interests are exactly the same as those of the rest of the human race. Your paramount interest, if you are aware of the situation, must be to preserve the existence of mankind by preventing a great war. It is clearly the duty of men of science to bring the facts home, as far as lies in their power, to the governments and peoples of both East and West. This is no easy task. The governments of both East and West, whether from ignorance or from motives of prestige, are engaged in trying to persuade their populations that thermonuclear weapons will destroy the enemy but not themselves. *The Red Star,* the official military organ of the Soviet government, published several articles on methods of defense against thermonuclear weapons. These articles were so absurd that one could hardly believe their authors to be sincere. It seemed obvious that the purpose of the articles was to deceive people in Russia as to the perils to which they would be exposed. I am afraid that the schemes for civil defense put forward in America and Britain are equally misleading. I hope that this is because the authorities are ignorant and not because they are dishonest.

Clearly, scientists both of the East and of the West have an imperative duty: namely, the duty of bringing home to the protagonists the fact that the time is past for swashbuckling and boasting and campaigns of bluff which, if the bluff is called, can end only in utter disaster. I have been glad to see a lead given by a small number of men of science of the highest eminence, representing many countries and all creeds, Americans, Western Europeans, Poles and Japanese. I have rejoiced to see these men issue a clear statement as to what is likely to happen in a great war; and I should wish them to invite all other men of science, in all countries, to subscribe to this statement.

I am aware that this will involve a certain degree of heroism and self-sacrifice. But there will be a reward which brave men should find sufficient: the reward of preserving uprightness and self-respect in the face of danger. These virtues are common in battle, and men of science should be able to show them also in a conflict with ignorance and ferocity. Science has fought great fights in former centuries against the embattled forces of obscurantism. In the nineteenth century it seemed as though science were victorious, but the victory is in danger of proving illusory. If science is to do its duty by mankind, men of science must once again face martyrdom and obloquy and the accusation of indifference to moral values. Perhaps their prestige may suffice to save them from the worst penalties for their courage, but of this we cannot be confident. What we can say with confidence is that it is not worth while to prolong a slavish and cowardly existence for a few miserable years while those who know the magnitude of the impending catastrophe wait for that radioactive death that is in store for them as well as for others.

A difficult readjustment in the scientists' conception of duty is imperatively necessary. As Lord Adrian said in his address to the British Association, "Unless we are ready to give up some of our old loyalties, we may be forced into a fight which might end the human race." This matter of loyalty is the crux. Hitherto, in the East and in the West alike, most scientists, like most other people, have felt that loyalty to their own state is paramount. They have no longer a right to feel this. Loyalty to the human race must take its place. Everyone in the West will at once admit this as regards Soviet scientists. We are shocked that Kapitza, who was Rutherford's favorite pupil, was willing, when the Soviet government refused him permission to return to Cambridge, to place his scientific skill at the disposal of those who wished to spread communism by means of H-bombs. We do not so readily apprehend a similar failure of duty on our own side. I do not wish to be thought to suggest treachery, since that is only a transference of loyalty to another national state; I am suggesting a very different thing: that scientists the world over should join in enlightening mankind as to the perils of a great war and in devising methods for its prevention. I urge with all the emphasis at my disposal that this is the duty of scientists in East and West alike. It is a difficult duty, and one likely to entail penalties for those who perform it. But, after all, it is the labors of scientists which have caused the danger and on this account, if on no other, scientists must do everything in their power to save mankind from the madness which they have made possible.

Science from the dawn of history, and probably longer, has been intimately associated with war. I imagine that when our ancestors descended from the trees they were victorious over the arboreal conservatives because flints were sharper than coconuts. To come to more recent times, Archimedes was respected for his scientific defense of Syracuse against the Romans; Leonardo obtained employment under the Duke of Milan because of his skill in fortification, though he did mention in a postscript that he could also paint a bit; Galileo similarly derived an income from the Grand Duke of Tuscany because of his skill in calculating the trajectories of projectiles. In the French Revolution, those scientists who were not guillotined devoted themselves to making new explosives. There is therefore no departure from tradition in the present-day scientists' manufacture of A-bombs and H-bombs. All that is new is the extent of their destructive skill.

I do not think that men of science can cease to regard the disinterested pursuit of knowledge as their primary duty. It is true that new knowledge and new skills are sometimes harmful in their effects, but scientists cannot profitably take account of this fact since the effects are impossible to foresee. We cannot blame Columbus because the discovery of the Western Hemisphere spread throughout the Eastern Hemisphere an appallingly devastating plague. Nor can we blame James Watt for

the Dust Bowl, although if there had been no steam engines
and no railways the West would not have been so carelessly or
so quickly cultivated. To see that knowledge is wisely used is
primarily the duty of statesmen, not of men of science; but it is
part of the duty of men of science to see that important knowledge is widely disseminated and is not falsified in the interests
of this or that propaganda.

Scientific knowledge has its dangers; but so has every great
thing. And over and beyond the dangers with which it threatens
the present, it opens up as nothing else can the vision of a possible happy world, a world without poverty, without war, with
little illness. And, what is perhaps more than all, when science
has mastered the forces which mold human character, it will
be able to produce populations in which few suffer from destructive fierceness and in which the great majority regard other
people, not as competitors to be feared, but as helpers in a
common task. Science has only recently begun to apply itself
to human beings, except in their purely physical aspect. Such
science as exists in psychology and anthropology has hardly
begun to affect political behavior or private ethics. The minds
of men remain attuned to a world that is fast disappearing. The
changes in our physical environment require, if they are to
bring well-being, correlative changes in our beliefs and habits.
If we cannot effect these changes, we shall suffer the fate of the
dinosaurs who could not live on dry land. I think it is the duty
of science—I do not say of every individual man of science—to
study the means by which we can adapt ourselves to the new
world. There are certain things that the world quite obviously
needs: tentativeness, as opposed to dogmatism, in our beliefs;
an expectation of co-operation, rather than competition, in
social relations; a lessening of envy and collective hatred. These
are things which education could produce without much difficulty. They are not things adequately sought in the education
of the present day.

It is to progress in the human sciences that we must look to
undo the evils which have resulted from a knowledge of the
physical world hastily and superficially acquired by populations

unconscious of the changes in themselves that the new knowledge has made imperative. The road to a happier world than
any known in the past lies open before us if atavistic destructive
passions can be kept in leash while the necessary adaptations
are made. Fears are inevitable in our time, but hopes are equally
rational and far more likely to bear good fruit. We must learn
to think rather less of the dangers to be avoided than of the
good that will lie within our grasp if we can believe in it and let
it dominate our thoughts. Science, whatever unpleasant consequences it may have by the way, is in its very nature a liberator,
a liberator of bondage to physical nature and, in time to come,
a liberator from the weight of destructive passions. We are on
the threshold of utter disaster or unprecedentedly glorious
achievement. No previous age has been fraught with problems
so momentous; and it is to science that we must look for a happy
issue.

The Library of Liberal Arts